International Baccalaureate Chemistry Option B Biochemistry

CW00408056

Contents

Introduction

Introduction to the Biochemistry option

The aim of this option is to give an understanding of the chemistry of important molecules found in living organisms. There is also an attempt to raise awareness of some environmental implications of the biochemistry.

This option involves the study of some large molecules. You are not required to memorise them, but you are expected to recognise functional groups and types of bonding within and between them. The structures of many of these molecules are given in sections 33, 34 and 35 of the *Chemistry data booklet*. You should familiarise yourself with these tables as part of your revision.

Students who have also studied HL or SL Biology will find themselves familiar with the background to this topic and there is inevitably a certain amount of overlap. However the exam questions are set to emphasise the chemistry. To obtain full marks your answers must go beyond the biological roles of the molecules and identify the chemical detail, such as the types of bonding and organic functional groups.

I am very grateful to my wife, Jane, for her helpful comments. Thanks also to all my IB chemistry students, both at school and at OSC.

Using this revision guide

This guide covers the key points of the syllabus for this option in a concise form to help you check your knowledge and understanding of the ideas. There are also lots of diagrams to help you visualise how these large molecules are arranged. Make sure that you also have a copy of the published syllabus, and use this as a checklist as you go through each section.

This guide also includes 'Exam tips', worked examples of calculations, explanations of key terms and revision questions at the end of each chapter. The revision questions are similar to those that might get asked on Paper 3 of the IB HL or SL Chemistry exam. The answers to all the revision questions are given at the end of this guide.

Topics for Standard and Higher Level in this guide

Standard Level students only have to cover some of the topics in this guide. These are given in sections B1 to B6 of the syllabus given in the *Chemistry Subject Guide*. The additional topics for Higher Level are covered in sections B7 to B10 as follows.

- B7 is an extension to topic B2 Proteins and enzymes.
- B8 Nucleic acids is a stand-alone topic
- B9 Biological pigments is a stand-alone topic
- B10 Stereochemistry in biomolecules contains small extensions to topics B2 Proteins and Enzymes, B3 Lipids and B4 Carbohydrates. There is also a stand-alone sub-topic on vision chemistry.

In this guide, the HL topics that are extensions of SL topics have been covered at the point where they naturally follow on from the SL topics. The two stand-alone HL topics are then covered at the end of the guide.

Higher Level topics are clearly marked by shading of the text as shown here.

Using past IB Chemistry papers

Past IB papers and their markschemes are a valuable aid to your revision. The more practice you get, the better your performance will be in the final exam. The following routine will help you make the best use of them.

1. Revise certain topics (or all topics if the exam is near).

2. Try to answer the questions on the topics you have revised in the same amount of time you would have in the exam (about 1½ minutes per mark) without looking at the markscheme.

3. Now use your class notes or this revision guide to look up and learn this missing material and improve/correct your answers.

4. Finally look at the markscheme and try to mark your answers as if you are the examiner. You may find that even though you knew all the material, you still did not get full marks. If not, ask yourself why not? Common reasons are:
   - you misunderstood what the question was asking for
   - you did not write enough detail to get all the marks
   - you did not use the right key words to get the mark(s).

Recent changes to the Biochemistry Option syllabus

If you are using past papers from before May 2016, then the questions will be testing a different syllabus. Material has been deleted and new material added (including some that used to be in other options). There are also a few changes between HL and SL material. The table below summarises the main changes with HL topics shaded.

No longer on the syllabus	New for 2016 papers onwards
Calculation of the energy value of a food	The terms: metabolism, anabolism, catabolism, photosynthesis
Functions of proteins in the body	Calculation of pH of buffer solutions (was in AHL Topic 18)
	Determination of protein concentration using UV-vis spectroscopy (was in the old Option A)
	Enzymes and effect of substrate concentration, temperature, pH and heavy metals (was HL, now SL)
Functions of lipids in the body	Effect of structure on the melting points of fats and oils (was in the old Option F)
Omega-3 and omega-6 labelling of fatty acids.	Hydrolytic and oxidative rancidity of fats (was in the old Option F)
Structures of the polysaccharides: amylose, amylopectin and glycogen.	The term: Haworth projection
Details of compounds in dietary fibre	Identification of D and L stereoisomers of monosaccharides
Macronutrients and micronutrients	Effect of heat on vitamins
Minerals	The terms: xenobiotics, host-guest chemistry, biomagnification, green chemistry
Hormones and oral contraceptives	Biodegradable plastics and use of starch
	Enzymes used for oil spills and biodegradable detergents
Transcription of DNA to RNA and translation to give polypeptides.	Role of hydrophobic bases in the stability of the DNA double helix
DNA profiling	Negative charge on DNA and histones
	DNA replication
	Benefits and concerns of GM foods (was in the old Option F)
	Haemoglobin oxygen dissociation curve and effects of heat, acid and CO_2
	Foetal haemoglobin
	Colour in pigments due to conjugated π-bond systems (was in Option F)
	Effect of pH and metal ions on colour of anthocyanins (was in Option F)
	Roles of chlorophyll and carotenoids in photosynthesis
Aerobic and anaerobic respiration	Paper and TLC to separate pigments
Role of Cu^{2+} in electron transport	Role of Fe^{3+}/Fe^{2+} in cytochromes
	Roles of opsin, rhodopsin and retinal in vision chemistry

OSC Revision Guide

1 Introduction to biochemistry (Syllabus section B1)

Biochemistry describes the chemistry that occurs within living organisms. The chemical reactions that keep a living organism alive are known as **metabolic** reactions. These reactions take place in the aqueous environment that is found inside biological cells, or in the fluids that surround the cells. In these environments, factors such as the concentration of different substances, pH, and temperature are highly controlled by the living organism. The majority of metabolic reactions are catalysed by enzymes (see chapter 2).

Biological molecules are typically organic compounds, many of which are large and complex. However, small inorganic molecules and metal ions are also involved in some metabolic reactions. The diverse functions of biological molecules depend not only on the reactivity of their functional groups, but also on their structures and shapes.

Metabolism in which larger molecules are synthesised from smaller precursors is called **anabolism**, while the breakdown of the larger molecules is called **catabolism**. The first step in anabolism is the **photosynthesis** of glucose from carbon dioxide and water by plants and algae. This is an endothermic reaction that requires energy from visible light to break the strong bonds in water and carbon dioxide.

$$6CO_2 \ + \ 6H_2O \ \underset{\text{respiration}}{\overset{\text{photosynthesis}}{\rightleftharpoons}} \ C_6H_{12}O_6 \ + \ 6O_2 \qquad \Delta H = +2803 \text{ kJmol}^{-1}$$

Exam Tip

Questions often ask you to use given structures to draw the products of condensation or hydrolysis. This skill is worth practising.

Glucose is either built up into larger molecules by further anabolic reactions (see below), or it can be broken down by **respiration** to provide energy for plant or animal cells. Respiration is a complex set of metabolic reactions involving oxidation of the glucose. This process releases energy as the strong bonds in carbon dioxide and water are reformed. The balance between photosynthesis and respiration is also important for maintaining constant levels of oxygen and carbon dioxide in the atmosphere.

Another important type of anabolic reaction is the formation of large biopolymers by **condensation** reactions in which H and OH are removed from functional groups on the monomers allowing them to join, forming water as a by-product.

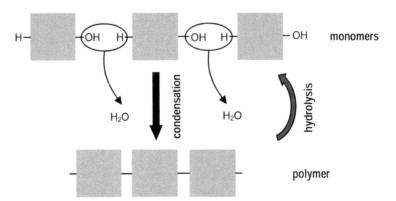

Examples include the formation of polypeptides from amino acids (see chapter 2) and the formation of polysaccharides from monosaccharides (see chapter 4). Polymers such as these can be broken down by **hydrolysis**, which splits water and uses the H and OH to reform monomers again.

2 Proteins and enzymes (Syllabus sections B2 and B7, plus amino acid stereochemistry from section B10)

Structure of 2-amino acids

Proteins are made from the 20 different 2-amino acids. Their names and structural formulae are given in Section 33 of the *Data booklet* as in the example below.

Common name	Symbol	Structural formula	pH of isoelectric point
arginine	Arg	$H_2N-CH-COOH$ $\quad\quad\mid$ $CH_2\text{-}CH_2\text{-}CH_2\text{-}NH-C-NH_2$ $\quad\quad\quad\quad\quad\quad\quad\parallel$ $\quad\quad\quad\quad\quad\quad\quad NH$	10.8

Chemistry data booklet, 2015, © IBO

They all contain a basic amine group (usually $-NH_2$) and the acidic carboxyl group ($-COOH$) attached to a central carbon atom. When amino acids are named systematically, this carbon is the second carbon in the chain that starts with the carboxylic acid carbon, hence the name: 2-amino acids.

$H_2N-CH-COOH$
$\quad\quad\mid$
$\quad\quad R$

The symbol 'R' represents a side chain that is different for each 2-amino acid.

With the exception of glycine, which has just 'H' as its R group, all the other 19 naturally occurring amino acids are chiral, as they have four different groups bonded tetrahedrally to the second carbon. This means that they exist in two mirror image configurations that are stereoisomers of each other. Only the L-configuration is found naturally in proteins.

L-alanine   D-alanine

HL ONLY

Acid-base properties of 2-amino acids

The presence of both acidic and a basic groups means that amino acids are classified as being **amphoteric** (or more specifically as being **amphiprotic**). This is because they can exist as cations by the amine group accepting a proton, or as anions by the carboxyl group donating a proton, or as **zwitterions** when both groups are ionised. A zwitterion is a salt with both a positive and a negative charge on the same molecule.

$H_2N-CH-COOH \longrightarrow {}^+H_3N-CH-COO^-$
$\quad\quad\mid \quad\quad\quad\quad\quad\quad\quad\quad\quad\mid$
$\quad\quad R \quad\quad\quad\quad\quad\quad\quad\quad\quad R$

H⁺ gained   H⁺ lost   zwitterion

Amino acids typically exist as zwitterions when solid or dissolved in water. The presence of charged groups explains their good solubility in water, as strong ion-dipole forces can form between the charged groups and polar water molecules. Also strong ionic bonding between the zwitterions in the solid also means that they have higher melting points than other organic molecules of their size.

OSC Revision Guide

The ionisation of amino and carboxyl groups depends on the pH of the solution.

pH	1	2	3	4	5	6	7	8	9	10	11	12	13	14
amino group	all are NH_3^+					most are NH_3^+			H^+ gained ←			all are NH_2		
carboxyl group	all are COOH		H^+ lost →			most are COO^-						all are COO^-		
overall charge	positive					neutral						negative		

↑
isoelectric point

For most 2-amino acids the total number of positive and negative charges is equal at around pH 6 as shown above. The pH at which there is no overall charge is called the **isoelectric point**. Therefore at a pH lower than the isoelectric point, the amino acid will have an overall positive charge, and vice versa. The value of the isoelectric point varies slightly depending on how the side group (R) affects the strength of the acidic and basic groups. 2-Amino acids with additional acidic or basic functional groups on their side groups will have even lower or higher isoelectric points. Isoelectric points for the 20 naturally occurring 2-amino acids are given in section 33 of the *Data booklet*.

Buffer solutions

Amino acids and proteins can act as **buffers** in solution. A buffer solution is one that resists changes in pH when small amounts of acid or alkali are added. Amino acids and proteins have an important natural role in maintaining the required pH within cells and other fluids. Buffer solutions can be also made from other weak acids and bases. Buffer solutions are used widely in medicine and the food industry to control the pH of liquids in contact with the body.

A buffer solution is composed of a mixture of a weak acid and its conjugate base, or a mixture of a weak base and its conjugate acid. Either way, as long as both species are present in reasonable amounts, the equilibrium between the protonated and deprotonated species will be able to respond to the addition of H^+ ions or OH^- ions. This happens as the equilibrium position shifts to oppose the change, removing the added ions, and so minimising the effect of the added acid or alkali. For a typical weak acid HA:

$$HA \rightleftharpoons H^+ + A^-$$

Any added H^+ ions are removed as the equilibrium can shift **left** in response, i.e. $H^+ + A^- \rightarrow HA$

Any added OH^- ions are removed as they combine with H^+ ions to give water: $H^+ + OH^- \rightarrow H_2O$. The resulting decrease in $[H^+]$ causes the equilibrium to shift **right** in response, i.e. $HA \rightarrow H^+ + A^-$. Overall this gives: $HA + OH^- \rightarrow H_2O + A^-$.

The pH of a buffer solution can be calculated as long as the pK_a of the weak acid is known, as well as the relative concentrations of the acid and its conjugate base in the mixture. The *Data booklet* gives pK_a values for a range of organic acids in Section 21. The necessary mathematical expression, known as the Henderson-Hasselbalch equation, is given in section 1 of the *Data booklet*.

$$pH = pK_a + \log\left(\frac{[A^-]}{[HA]}\right)$$

Worked example 2.1

A buffer solution is made by dissolving 3.84 g of sodium propanoate (C_2H_5COONa) into 100 cm³ of a 0.200 mol dm⁻³ solution of propanoic acid. Use the pK_a value for propanoic acid from the *Data booklet* to calculate the pH of the buffer solution.

Amount of sodium propanoate, $n = m/M_r$ = 3.84 g ÷ 96.07 g mol⁻¹ = 0.0400 mol

Concentration of sodium propanoate, $c = n/v$ = 0.0400 mol ÷ 0.100 dm³ = 0.400 mol dm⁻³

pK_a for propanoic acid (from *Data booklet*) = 4.87

pH of the buffer solution = pK_a + log ([A-]/[HA]) = 4.87 + log (0.400/0.200)

= 4.87 + log 2 = 4.87 + 0.301 = **5.17**

It is quite common for buffer solutions to be made by partially neutralising an excess of the weak acid with a strong base. This creates the conjugate base of the acid as a product of the reaction. The amount of weak acid remaining in the mixture must be calculated by subtracting the amount of acid that has reacted from the amount originally present.

Worked example 2.2

A buffer solution is made by adding 400cm³ of 0.0500 mol dm⁻³ sodium hydroxide to 100 cm³ of a 0.500 mol dm⁻³ solution of methanoic acid. Use the pK_a value for methanoic acid from the *Data booklet* to calculate the pH of the buffer solution.

Initial amount of HCOOH, $n = c \times v$ 0.100 dm³ x 0.500 mol dm⁻³ = 0.0500 mol

Added amount of NaOH, $n = c \times v$ 0.400 dm³ x 0.0500 mol dm⁻³ = 0.0200 mol

Reaction:	HCOOH	+ NaOH	→	HCOONa	+ H₂O
Initial amounts:	0.0500 mol	0.0200 mol		0 mol	
Final amounts:	0.0300 mol	0 mol		0.0200 mol	

pK_a for methanoic acid (from *Data booklet*) = 3.75

pH of the buffer solution = pK_a + log ([A-]/[HA]) = 3.75 + log (0.0200/0.0300)

= 3.75 + log 0.667 = 3.75 + - 0.176 = **3.57**

> **Exam Tip**
>
> Note that in this example the ratio of moles of A⁻ and HA has been used in the Henderson-Hasselbalch equation. There is no need to spend time calculating the concentrations as they would have the same ratio.

The two examples above involve buffers made from weak acids. When a buffer is made from a weak base, all the same principles apply. You can still use the Henderson-Hasselbalch equation, but you have to remember that A⁻ now refers to the base, and HA now refers to the conjugate acid. Also if you are given the pK_b of the base, this must be converted to the pK_a of the conjugate acid using the expression:

$$pK_a = 14 - pK_b.$$

Note that this only applies at 25°C, when pK_w = exactly 14. For temperatures other than 25°C, a new value of pK_w would have to be calculated using the values of Kw given in section 23 of the *Data booklet*.

OSC Revision Guide

Exam Tip

Notice how the ratio A⁻/HA has been replaced by B/BH⁺ for the base. Take care to get this ratio the right way around.

Worked example 2.3

A basic buffer solution is made from the amino acid glycine. The amine group in glycine has a pK_b of 4.4. Calculate the ratio of the concentration of the basic form (B) to the acidic form (BH⁺) needed to create a pH of 9.0.

$$pK_a \text{ for the conjugate acid } = 14 - 4.4 = 9.6$$

$$\text{pH of the buffer solution } = pK_a + \log(\,[A\text{-}]/[HA]\,) = pK_a + \log(\,[B]/[BH^+]\,)$$

$$9.0 = 9.6 + \log(\,[B]/[BH^+]\,)$$

$$-0.6 = \log(\,[B]/[BH^+]\,)$$

$$[B]/[BH^+] = 10^{-0.6} = 0.25$$

Assay of proteins using UV-visible spectroscopy

The concentration of a protein in aqueous solution is typically very low. This makes determination of the concentration difficult using titration. However, certain amino acids will absorb UV light at a specific wavelength due to the presence of a benzene ring in their side chain. For example, tyrosine and tryptophan will absorb UV light well at a wavelength around 220 nm. The relationship between the amount of light absorbed and the concentration is given by the **Beer-Lambert law**. This is given in Section 1 of the *Data Booklet*.

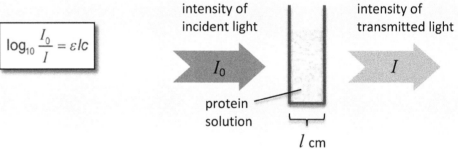

$$\log_{10}\frac{I_0}{I} = \varepsilon l c$$

intensity of incident light I_0

protein solution

intensity of transmitted light I

l cm

The spectrometer measures the intensity of the light transmitted through the protein sample (I) compared to the intensity of the incident light (I_0) (usually determined using a blank sample).

$\log_{10}(I_0/I)$ is known as the **absorbance** (A) of the solution and this is directly proportional to the concentration (c) of the protein solution. The expression can be therefore simplified to give:

$$\textbf{absorbance } (A) = \varepsilon\, l\, c$$

The path length (l) is the width of the container that the light is shining through. This is often 1 cm, and will be depend on the particular spectrometer being used. ε is the molar absorption coefficient. This is constant for the particular protein being measured. However, it is not necessary to use these values if a **calibration curve** is created by measuring the absorbance of a set of solutions of the protein covering a range of concentration. As absorbance is proportional to concentration, this should be a straight line.

An example of a calibration curve is shown below.

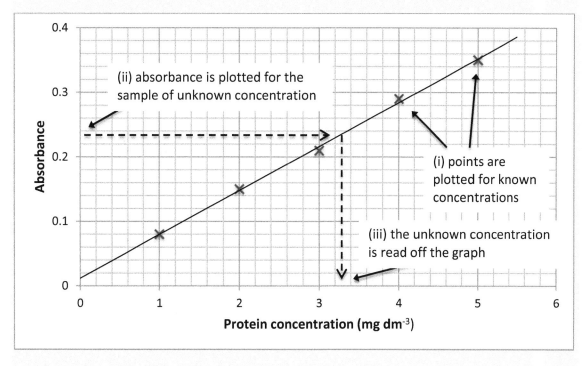

Key steps in the method are as follows:

1. Make up a range of different solutions of known protein concentrations.

2. Measure the absorbance for each concentration.

3. Plot a calibration curve of absorbance against concentration, as in (i) above.

4. Measure the absorbance of the protein solution of unknown concentration.

5. Using the graph, deduce the value of the unknown concentration from its absorbance, as in (ii) and (iii) above.

Worked example 2.4

A protein sample transmits 68% of the UV light at 220nm transmitted through a blank sample. Using the calibration curve above, determine the concentration of the protein.

$I = 68\%, I_0 = 100\%$

$A = \log(I_0/I) = \log(100/68) = 0.167$

Using the calibration curve, c = **2.3 mg dm^{-3}**

HL ONLY

Polypeptides

2-Amino acids form polypeptides by condensation polymerisation (see chapter 1). This links the amino acids together by a carboxamide group, which is often called an amide or peptide linkage in this context. Polypeptide chains can be any length. For example, the formation of the tripeptide: Phe-Ala-Cys, is shown below.

Protein structure

Proteins are formed by the folding of one or more polypeptide chains into a unique 3-dimensional shape. There are four levels of protein structure, each involving particular types of bond or intermolecular force.

1. The primary structure of a protein is the sequence of 2-amino acids in the polypeptide chain(s), starting from the nitrogen end. The strong covalent bond in the amide linkage is formed by the condensation reaction above.

2. The secondary structure describes two ways that the polypeptide chains often fold due to hydrogen bonds between the oxygens and hydrogens of amide linkages of different parts of the chain. The **α-helix** is formed by the chain coiling so that hydrogen bonds can form between linkages above or below them in the coil. The side chains all point outwards and each turn of the helix is 3.6 amino acids. The **β-pleated sheet** is formed by the chains running parallel to each other with the hydrogen bonds forming across the sheet between adjacent linkages. In this arrangement, the side chains point alternately above and below the sheet.

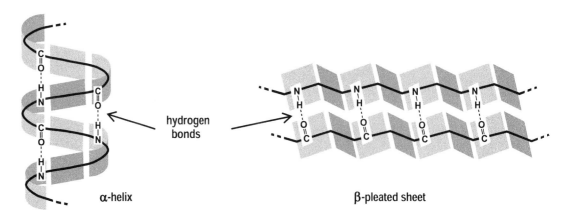

α-helix   hydrogen bonds   β-pleated sheet

3. The tertiary structure of a protein describes how the whole polypeptide chain (including any regions of α-helix and β-pleated sheet) is folded to give the overall 3-D shape of the protein. The tertiary structure is maintained by different bonds and intermolecular forces between the side chains of the 2-amino acids.

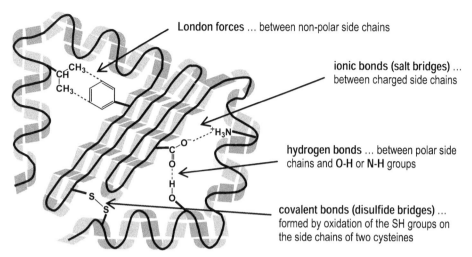

London forces ... between non-polar side chains

ionic bonds (salt bridges) ... between charged side chains

hydrogen bonds ... between polar side chains and **O-H** or **N-H** groups

covalent bonds (disulfide bridges) ... formed by oxidation of the SH groups on the side chains of two cysteines

4. Many proteins are composed of more than one polypeptide chain. The quaternary structure describes how the polypeptide chains are joined. It is maintained by the same types of bonds and forces as the tertiary structure.

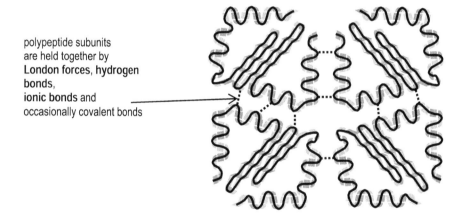

polypeptide subunits are held together by **London forces, hydrogen bonds**, **ionic bonds** and occasionally covalent bonds

Globular and fibrous proteins

The 3-dimensional shape of a protein determines its role in the living organism. The type of protein shown above is described as **globular** as the polypeptide chains are folded back on themselves to form a roughly spherical shape. Examples of globular proteins include: haemoglobin, enzymes, immunoproteins (antibodies) and hormones. These typically carry out functions related to metabolic processes within the fluids inside or outside the cells. Other proteins are described as **fibrous**, when the polypeptide chains remain extended and interlock with each other. This creates a tough insoluble material that has structural uses within the organism. Examples of fibrous proteins include: muscle proteins, collagen in connective tissue, and keratin in skin, hair and nails.

OSC Revision Guide

Analysis of proteins by paper chromatography and gel electrophoresis

Amino acids can be separated out and identified by paper chromatography or gel electrophoresis - or sometimes a combination of both. These techniques rely on differing physical and chemical properties of the substances, such as relative solubility, isoelectric point and size of the molecules. To use these methods to analyse a protein, the peptide linkages must be first hydrolysed by heating with dilute hydrochloric acid to give a mixture of the individual amino acids.

The mixture of amino acids is analysed by **paper chromatography** as follows:

1. A spot of the hydrolysed mixture, plus spots of known amino acids as references, are placed side by side along a line drawn parallel to one end of the paper.

2. This end of the paper is then placed in a suitable solvent and left so that the solvent seeps up through the paper. The amino acids will separate because of their differing solubilities in the solvent.

3. When the solvent front has nearly reached the other side of the paper, it is removed from the solvent and left to dry.

4. The paper is sprayed with a **locating agent** such as ninhydrin to make the amino acids visible as coloured spots.

5. The R_f **value** of the amino acids in the mixture can be calculated and compared with that of the reference substances.

The R_f value of an amino acid is calculated by:

$$\frac{\textbf{distance moved by the amino acid}}{\textbf{distance moved by solvent}}$$

The distances are measured from the chromatogram, as shown for the spot due to one of the three amino acids in the mixture.

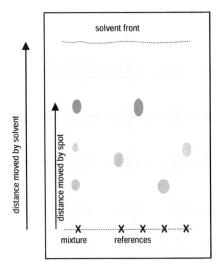

The mixture of amino acids is analysed by **gel electrophoresis** as follows:

1.   The hydrolysed mixture is dissolved in a buffer solution, chosen to give a good separation of the amino acids.

2.   Spots of this mixture, plus any references, are placed side by side along a line across the centre of the gel.

3.   Electrodes are attached at each end of the gel. The voltage causes the amino acids to move in a direction depending on their overall charge at the chosen pH. The size of the molecules can also affect the rate of movement through the gel.

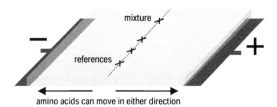

4.   The gel is sprayed with a locating agent such as ninhydrin to make the amino acids visible.

5.   The direction and distance moved by the amino acids in the mixture is compared to that of the reference amino acids and their known isoelectric points.

Note that as amino acids become more positively charged at lower pH values, an amino acid or protein will move towards the negative electrode if its isoelectric point is below that of the buffer solution. Similarly if the isoelectric point is above the pH of the buffer solution, it will be negatively charged overall and so move towards the positive electrode.

Revision questions

2.1   Draw the two stereoisomers of the amino acid serine (HL)   [2]

2.2   The amino acid alanine has a melting point of 258°C. Lactamide is a structural isomer of alanine with formula $CH_3CH(OH)CONH_2$ and has a melting point of 75°C. Explain why the melting point of alanine is significantly higher than that of lactamide. [3]

2.3   Draw the structure of the amino acid phenylalanine at pH 2.5, pH 5.5 and pH 9.5.   [3]

2.4   A buffer solution made from a mixture of benzoic acid and sodium benzoate needs to have a pH of 4.0. Calculate the ratio of benzoic acid to sodium benzoate required to obtain this pH. [3]

2.5   Draw the structure of the tripeptide: Ser-Asp-Met.   [2]

2.6   Draw the structure of two dipeptides that could be formed from alanine and and lysine.   [2]

2.7   Describe the bonds involved in maintaining primary, secondary and tertiary structure.   [5]

2.8   Explain how the amino acid composition of a protein is analysed by paper chromatography.   [6]

2.9   A mixture of histidine, valine and glutamic acid is analysed by electrophoresis at pH 6.0. Predict which electrode, if any, each amino acid would move towards.   [3]

2.10 State an example of a globular and a fibrous protein.   [2]

active ← site

enzyme

Enzymes

Enzymes are biological catalysts. Most enzymes are made from proteins. Part of the protein forms an **active site**, which binds specifically to the reactant(s). The activity of the enzyme depends on the precise 3-D conformation of the protein that results from the tertiary and quaternary structure. This means that enzymes can be inhibited by factors that affect tertiary structure, such as high temperature, pH changes and the presence of heavy metal ions.

The typical relationship between substrate (reactant) concentration and the rate of an enzyme catalysed reaction is shown by the graph below.

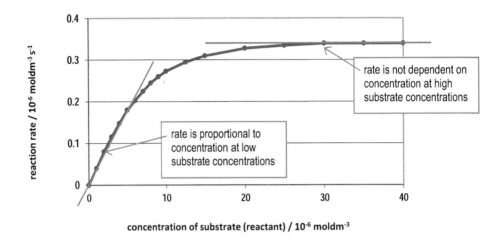

The graph shows that at lower substrate concentrations, the rate of reaction changes in proportion to the substrate concentration. However at higher substrate concentrations, the rate is less affected by a change in substrate concentration. If the substrate concentration is very high then any change does not affect the rate at all.

The following mechanism has been suggested to explain this graph.

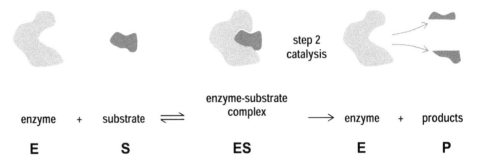

An enzyme-substrate complex, ES, is formed by the substrate joining to the enzyme at the **active site**. This part of the enzyme molecule has a specific shape and certain functional groups precisely placed to bind the substrate molecule using various intermolecular forces. While the substrate is bound to the enzyme, the reaction can now proceed via a mechanism with lower activation energy than without the enzyme. Those molecules that have kinetic energy greater than this lower E_a can form the products.

An increase in substrate concentration will increase the frequency of collisions between the substrate and enzyme molecules. At low substrate concentrations, many of the enzyme molecules are not being used, so this will lead to a proportional increase in the rate. However at high substrate concentrations nearly all the enzyme molecules will have their active sites occupied by a substrate molecule and so none are available to bind with any additional colliding substrate molecules. This means that a change in substrate concentration will have very little effect on the rate.

Inhibition of enzymes

This can happen in a number of ways as follows. In most cases the inhibition results from a loss of the correct 3-D tertiary structure needed for the enzyme to function properly.

- **Temperature changes** – too cold and too few molecules have kinetic energy $\geq E_a$ (as for any chemical reaction), too hot and the protein is denatured and loses its tertiary structure.

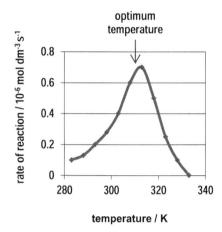

- **pH changes** – too high will deprotonate the charged $-NH_3^+$ groups, and too low will protonate the charged $-COO^-$ groups, both of which are essential for the ionic bonds needed to maintain the tertiary structure.
- **Heavy metal ions** can also inhibit enzymes, e.g. mercury(II) ions, which react with the $-SH$ groups that form the $-S-S-$ linkages needed to maintain the tertiary structure.

Enzyme Kinetics (HL)

The maximum rate possible for a certain amount of enzyme is known as V_{max}. Its value can be obtained from the graph of rate against the concentration of the substrate, as shown.

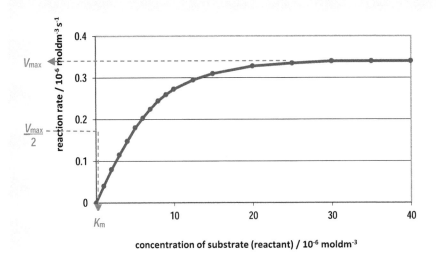

concentration of substrate (reactant) / 10^{-6} moldm^{-3}

Another value that can be measured from this graph is the **Michaelis constant (K_m)**. This is the concentration of substrate when the rate of reaction is half V_{max}. It is useful because it measures the strength of the binding between substrate and enzyme. A lower K_m indicates stronger binding, as the substrate concentration does not have to be as high for the rate to be nearer to V_{max}. Therefore the enzyme is more effective at lower concentrations of the substrate. Unlike V_{max}, the value of K_m does not depend on the enzyme concentration.

Competitive and non-competitive inhibition (HL)

Another type of enzyme inhibition is the presence of a **non-competitive inhibitor**, which is a molecule or ion that binds reversibly to the enzyme at a place other than the active site. The place of binding is called an **allosteric site**. This has the effect of changing the enzyme's tertiary structure, so affecting its activity. Non-competitive inhibitors play an important natural role in regulating the activity of enzymes. This sometimes takes the form of feedback or **product inhibition**, in which the product of a particular metabolic pathway inhibits an enzyme that catalyses a reaction at the start of the pathway. For example, the amino acid *isoleucine* is produced in some organisms from another amino acid, *threonine*, by a series of metabolic reactions. The first step in this reaction is catalysed by an enzyme called *threonine deaminase*. This enzyme is inhibited non-competitively by isoleucine, so regulating the production of isoleucine.

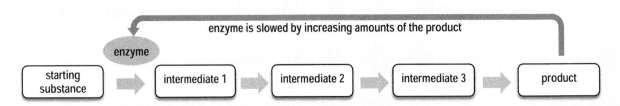

This keeps the concentration of the product relatively constant, as an increase in product concentration will result in a slowing of the enzyme, while a decrease in product concentration will allow the enzyme to speed up its production.

HL ONLY

Another way of reducing enzyme activity is the presence of a **competitive inhibitor**. Unlike a non-competitive inhibitor or factors like pH and heavy metal ions, this does not affect the tertiary structure, but reversibly binds to the enzyme at the active site without producing any products. It therefore competes with the substrate for the available active sites. At any given time, some of the enzyme molecules will be binding to the competitive inhibitor, so effectively reducing the concentration of active enzyme molecules.

The effect of competitive and non-competitive inhibitors can be compared on the graph of rate against substrate concentration.

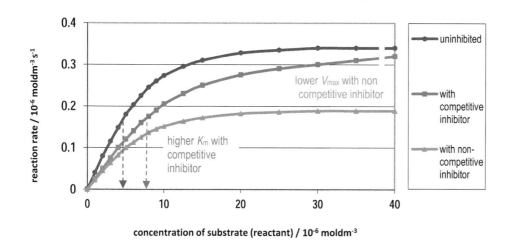

concentration of substrate (reactant) / 10^{-6} moldm^{-3}

It can be seen that a competitive inhibitor raises K_m, but V_{max} remains the same. Therefore the effect of competitive inhibitors can be overcome by increasing the substrate concentration. Non-competitive inhibitors will lower, V_{max} and often keep a similar K_m, as the change in tertiary structure has lowered the catalytic activity of the enzyme. Therefore it is not possible to restore the original activity by increasing substrate concentration.

Revision questions

2.11 Describe the general mechanism of enzyme action.   [3]

2.12 Sketch a graph to show the relationship between substrate concentration and enzyme activity. Explain the shape of the line.   [4]

2.13 State and explain three ways that enzyme activity can be reduced (other than by the presence of inhibitor molecules).   [6]

2.14 Glucokinase and hexokinase are both enzymes that catalyse the reaction of glucose with ATP. Glucokinase has $K_m = 1 \times 10^{-2}$ moldm^{-3} and hexokinase has $K_m = 1 \times 10^{-4}$ moldm^{-3}. State and explain which enzyme would be working closest to its maximum activity at normal blood glucose concentration of about 5×10^{-3} moldm^{-3}. [HL]   [2]

2.15 Explain the difference between competitive and non-competitive inhibitors of enzymes. State the effect of each type of inhibition on V_{max} and K_m. [HL]   [4]

OSC Revision Guide

3 Lipids

(Syllabus section B3, plus fatty acid stereochemistry from section B10)

Major functions of lipids

A lipid is a general term for a compound found naturally in plants or animals that is soluble in non-polar solvents. Three common types found in the human body are: **triglycerides** (fats and oils), **phospholipids** and **steroids**. Major functions of lipids found in the human body include:

* long term energy storage,
* thermal and electrical insulation,
* structural components of cell membranes (e.g. phospholipids and cholesterol),
* transporters of lipid soluble vitamins
* hormones (e.g. steroid sex hormones).

Triglycerides

Triglycerides are made from glycerol (i.e. propane-1,2,3-triol, an alcohol with three OH groups) and three **fatty acid** molecules. Natural fatty acids are straight chain carboxylic acids containing 4 to 22 carbon atoms. The structures of some fatty acids are given in the *Data booklet*, section 34 (see next page).

The condensation reaction to form the triglyceride creates an ester linkage. The hydrolysis of triglycerides to reform the fatty acids and glycerol can be catalysed either by digestive enzymes, or by heating in alkaline or acidic conditions.

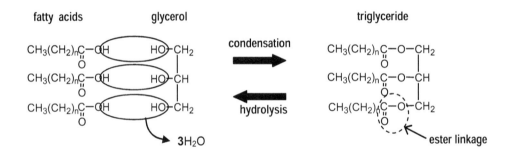

Phospholipids

These are similar to triglycerides except that one of the three fatty acids is replaced with a charged group that consists of phosphate group connected to another group. This allows phospholipids to form the bilayers that make up the structure of cell membranes. An example is *lecithin* where the phosphate is connected to a choline molecule – a positively charged amino alcohol with formula: $HOCH_2CH_2N(CH_3)_3^+$.

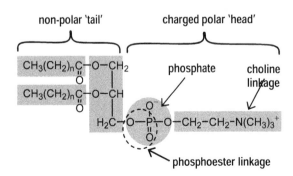

Note that the phosphate group is joined to both the glycerol and to the choline with a **phosphoester** linkage. This is similar in structure to the ester linkage used to join the glycerol to the fatty acids except the phosphoric acid has replaced the carboxylic acid in the normal ester linkage. This type of linkage also occurs in nucleotides and nucleic acids (see chapter 7). Hydrolysis of the phosphoester linkage reforms the dihydrogen phosphate ion, $H_2PO_4^-$ (or one of its alternative ionised forms, depending on pH).

Saturated and unsaturated fatty acids

Naturally occurring fatty acids may be **saturated**, **monounsaturated** (one C=C) or **polyunsaturated** (more than one C=C). The structures of some common fatty acids are given in the *Data booklet* in section 34. Some of these are shown below.

Chemistry data booklet, 2015, © IBO

Lipids		
Stearic acid	$CH_3(CH_2)_{16}COOH$	saturated
Oleic acid	$CH_3(CH_2)_7CH=CH(CH_2)_7COOH$	mono-unsaturated
Linoleic acid	$CH_3(CH_2)_4(CH=CHCH_2)_2(CH_2)_6COOH$	} poly-unsaturated
α-Linolenic acid	$CH_3CH_2(CH=CHCH_2)_3(CH_2)_6COOH$	

Iodine number

The degree of unsaturation in a triglyceride or fatty acid can be measured experimentally using the concept of **iodine number**. This is defined as: the number of grams of I_2 reacting with 100g of the fat/oil. The iodine number can be used to calculate the average number of carbon-carbon double bonds present per fat/oil molecule. To do this you need to know the relative molecular mass of the fat /oil and remember that one mole of iodine will react with one mole of C=C bonds in an addition reaction.

$$-\underset{H}{\underset{|}{C}}=\underset{H}{\underset{|}{C}}- \ + \ I_2 \longrightarrow -\underset{H}{\overset{I}{\underset{|}{\overset{|}{C}}}}-\underset{H}{\overset{I}{\underset{|}{\overset{|}{C}}}}-$$

Exam Tip

Iodine numbers are typically in the range 50 to 200 g/100g. If you get a value very different from this – check your working!

Worked example

A 0.500 g sample of an oil found in fish oil is found to react with 3.31×10^{-3} moles of iodine.

(a) Calculate the iodine number of the oil. M_r of iodine, I_2 = 126.90 x 2 = 253.80 gmol⁻¹

   Mass of iodine used = 3.31×10^{-3} mol x 253.80 gmol⁻¹ = 0.8401 g

   Mass of iodine needed per 100g oil = $0.8401 \text{ g} \times \dfrac{100 \text{ g}}{0.500 \text{ g}}$ = 420.0 g = **168 g/100 g**

(b) If the molecules of triglyceride in the fish oil have an average molar mass of 878 gmol⁻¹, calculate the average number of C=C double bonds per molecule.

   Moles of oil used in the sample = $\dfrac{0.500 \text{ g}}{878 \text{ gmol}^{-1}}$ = 5.695×10^{-4} mol

   Moles iodine, I_2 used per mole of oil = $\dfrac{3.31 \times 10^{-3} \text{ mol}}{5.695 \times 10^{-3} \text{ mol}}$ = 5.81 mol

   Iodine, I_2 reacts with C=C in a 1:1 ratio, so ∴ number of C=C per molecule of oil = **5.81**

With an average of nearly six C=C double bonds per triglyceride molecule in the previous example, there is an average of nearly two C=C bonds per fatty acid. This is not surprising, as fish oil is relatively unsaturated compared to many other naturally fats and oils.

Rancidity of fats

A fat is described as rancid when it develops a disagreeable odour and flavour, usually after being left exposed to the environment for a while. This happens due to chemical reactions, which break down the triglyceride molecules. There are two types of chemical reaction that lead to rancidity.

Hydrolytic rancidity

Hydrolysis of the ester bonds leads to the release of fatty acids and glycerol. Fatty acids have a sour taste due to their acidity, and some have quite unpleasant odours. Hydrolytic rancidity is more likely to occur when the fat is exposed to:

- **water**, which provides the solvent for hydrolysis reactions
- **acids**, such as citric or ethanoic acid in foods, which catalyse hydrolysis
- **microorganisms**, which contain lipase enzymes that catalyse hydrolysis
- **high temperatures**, which increase the rate of hydrolysis.

Oxidative rancidity

The C=C double bonds in unsaturated fatty acids can by oxidised by a free-radical reaction with oxygen gas. This eventually results in cleavage of the double bonds and the release of shorter chain fatty acids with particularly disagreeable odours. Oxidative rancidity is more likely to occur when the fat is exposed to:

- **air**, which provides the oxygen
- **light**, which promotes the formation of free-radicals.

Therefore fats and oils should ideally be stored at low temperatures, in a sterile environment, away from water and acids to prevent hydrolytic rancidity. Unsaturated fatty acids should also be kept away from sunlight and air. Antioxidants are often added to foods containing fats and oils to minimise amount of oxidative rancidity.

Melting points of fats and oils

Triglycerides are large molecules with the long hydrocarbon chains of the fatty acids making up the majority of molecule. Although there will be some dipole-dipole forces arising from the polar C=O and C-O bonds in the ester groups, the melting point of the fat will largely be determined by the strength of the London forces between the fatty acids chains of one molecule and the next. As with all molecules, the strength of these forces depends on two factors:

- **the size of the molecule** – longer fatty acid chains increases the chance of temporary dipoles forming, so increasing the melting point,
- **the shape of the molecule** – increasing the number of C=C bonds in *cis*-unsaturated fatty acids cause the fatty acid chains to 'kink', preventing them coming as close to each other, so decreasing the melting point.

The table below shows these effects by comparing the melting points of four fatty acids.

Name	No of C atoms	Formula	Type	Melting point /°C
Lauric acid	12	$CH_3(CH_2)_{10}COOH$	Saturated	44
Stearic acid	18	$CH_3(CH_2)_{16}COOH$	Saturated	70
Oleic acid	18	$CH_3(CH_2)_7C=C(CH_2)_7COOH$	Monounsaturated	14
α-Linolenic acid	18	$CH_3CH_2(CH=CHCH_2)_3(CH_2)_6COOH$	Polyunsaturated	-11

The effect of unsaturation on the melting point of fats and oils can also be seen by comparing a typical vegetable oil, such as olive oil, which has an iodine number of about 80g/100g, with butter, which has an iodine number of about 35g/100g. Olive oil is a liquid at room temperature due to its lower melting point, whereas butter is a solid with a higher melting point, as the more saturated fat in butter has fewer C=C bonds, so giving stronger London forces between the molecules.

Olive oil

Hydrogenation of fats (HL)
The C=C double bonds in naturally occurring unsaturated fats are mostly in the *cis* form. In the production of margarine from vegetable oils, the fats are **hydrogenated** to reduce the level of unsaturation in order to increase the melting point, so that the margarine has a consistency more like that of butter. This addition reaction is carried out by heating the oil with hydrogen gas over a nickel catalyst.

$$-C=C- \ + \ H_2 \ \xrightarrow[\text{heat}]{\text{Ni catalyst}} \ -C-C-$$

In this process, it is common that some but not all the C=C bonds are removed. This is known as **partial hydrogenation**.

Hydrogenation has the advantages of increasing the melting point to make the oil spreadable. It also decreases the rate of oxidative rancidity, as there are fewer C=C double bonds per molecule. However partial hydrogenation can also lead to the formation of **trans-fats**, which have been shown to lead to a number of health problems, including heart disease due to increased LDL cholesterol (see next page) and diabetes. *Trans*-fatty acids also take longer to metabolise, so accumulate more in the tissues, leading to obesity.

Trans fatty acids have higher melting points than their cis stereoisomer because the trans C=C bond does not 'kink' the chain in the same way. Instead, the overall shape of the chain is more regular like that of saturated fats, so they are able to get closer to each other, which increases the London forces between them. For example, *elaidic acid*, the *trans*-stereoisomer of oleic acid has a melting point of 43°C, compared to 16°C for oleic acid.

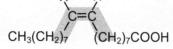

elaidic acid (*trans*-octadec-9-enoic acid)　　oleic acid (*cis*-octadec-9-enoic acid)

Fats in the diet

Triglycerides and cholesterol are transported around the body blood by **lipoproteins** which surround the water-insoluble lipids. There are two types of lipoproteins. High density lipoproteins (**HDL**) collect lipids from tissues and transport them to the liver. Low density lipoproteins (**LDL**) carry lipids from the liver out to the tissues. Elevated levels of LDL can lead to cholesterol being deposited in arteries. This impedes the flow of blood and can lead to an increased risk of a heart attack or stroke. The level of LDL in the blood is increased by:

- **saturated fats**, such as those found in meat or milk products,
- *trans*-**fatty acids** (see previous page).

In contrast, poly-unsaturated fatty acids, such as those found in plant or fish oils seem to lower the level LDL cholesterol and so reduce the risk of heart disease. This is why plant or fish oils are considered a healthier alternative to animal fats.

Lipids and carbohydrates as energy storage molecules

Both lipids and carbohydrates are used by living organisms to store energy. This energy can be released when needed by the organism, by oxidation of the compound during respiration (see Chapter 1). Lipids and carbohydrates differ in their roles as energy stores due to differences in their solubility in water and their energy density.

Solubility

Lipids are largely non-polar molecules, which do not dissolve easily in water. This makes them much less accessible to the water-soluble enzymes that break them down, ready for oxidation. The oxidation of lipids is therefore slower than for carbohydrates, which can dissolve easily in water, due to hydrogen bonding between O-H groups (see Chapter 4). Therefore if the organism needs energy quickly, carbohydrates are used as the primary energy store. An example would be glycogen stored in the muscles of animals.

Energy density

Lipids will release more energy per 100g on oxidation than carbohydrates. This is because lipids are more reduced than carbohydrates. During oxidation the C-C and C-H bonds in the compound are replaced with stronger C=O and O-H bonds in the carbon dioxide and water formed. The more reduced lipids have a much higher proportion of C-C and C-H bonds than the partially oxidised carbohydrates. This is because carbohydrates already contain more C=O, C-O and O-H bonds than triglycerides. Therefore organisms use lipids as an efficient energy store for the longer term, when the speed of release is not so important. Examples include oils in seeds and fat stores in mammals.

Steroids

Steroids are lipids with a characteristic fused ring structure, known as a **steroidal backbone**. Examples include cholesterol, the sex hormones and drugs such as anabolic steroids, used to increase muscle mass. The structure of cholesterol is given in the section 34 of the *Data Booklet*.

all steroids have this carbon skeleton, but the position of functional groups and double bonds varies

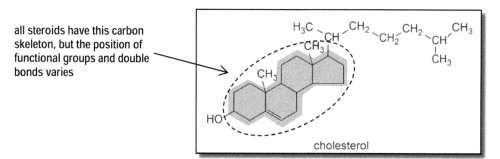

cholesterol

Chemistry data booklet, 2015, © IBO

Use and abuse of steroids

Anabolic steroids are synthetic hormones that mimic the action of testosterone to produce an increase in muscle mass. They are used medically to help patients recover from injury or starvation. They can also be used in bodybuilding to enhance strength or physique. The use of anabolic steroids to gain an advantage in competitive sports is banned by all major sporting bodies, including the International Olympic Committee. Rigorous testing of athletes is carried out and severe penalties are imposed as a deterrent to their use. The long-term use or excessive doses of anabolic steroids can also lead to health risks, such as reduction in fertility and male characteristics, due to lowering of natural testosterone levels.

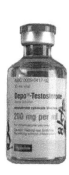

Revision questions

3.1 State the names of the three types of lipid found in the human body and state a major function of each type. [6]

3.2 Draw the structure of the products formed when the phospholipid lecithin (shown on page 18) is fully hydrolysed by heating with dilute acid. [4]

3.3 Describe two dietary factors that are thought to increase levels of LDL cholesterol in the blood and explain why this might be dangerous to the individual. [4]

3.4 Describe the structural difference between linoleic and α-linolenic acid and explain why it is important to include fats containing these two acids in a balanced diet. [3]

3.5 Define the term iodine number and calculate the number of C=C double bonds in a fatty acid with an iodine number of 90 and a molar mass of 282.5 gmol^{-1}. [3]

3.6 A triglyceride is formed using equal amounts of lauric acid, palmitic acid and oleic acid. State the type of reaction occurring and use the formulae in Section 34 of the Data Booklet to write a balanced equation. [4]

3.7 Olive oil has an energy value that is about twice that of cane sugar. Explain why the energy value of a fat is much higher than a carbohydrate. State and explain one disadvantage to an organism of using fat as an energy store. [4]

3.8 Use the data in the table on page 21 to predict the melting point of linoleic acid, which contains 18 carbon atoms and has two C=C bonds. Explain your reasoning. [2]

3.9 Discuss the advantages and disadvantages of hydrogenation of the fats used in food products (HL). [4]

3.10 Outline a medical and non-medical use of anabolic steroids. State two reasons why non-medical uses of anabolic steroids are controversial. [4]

4 Carbohydrates

(Syllabus section B4, plus stereochemistry from section B10)

Carbohydrates are compounds with a general formula $C_x(H_2O)_y$. In living organisms they are mainly used as immediate energy sources (e.g. glucose and fructose), as well as energy reserves (e.g. starch and glycogen).

Monosaccharides

Monosaccharides contain a carbonyl group (C=O) and at least two –OH groups. The simplest monosaccharides have molecular formula $C_3H_6O_3$. The carbon atoms are numbered from the end nearest to the carbonyl group as shown.

Monosaccharides may be aldehydes or ketones, depending on the position of the carbonyl group. Those that are aldehydes are known as **aldoses**, and the ketones are known as **ketoses**. Larger monosaccharides have additional H—C—OH groups.

Glucose and fructose are structural isomers with molecular formula $C_6H_{12}O_6$, which are given in section 35 of the *Data booklet*. Notice that glucose is an aldose and fructose is a ketose.

Chemistry data booklet, 2015, © IBO

straight chain glucose   straight chain fructose

These straight chain structures cyclise in solution to form rings by a reaction between the oxygen of carbon 5 and the carbonyl carbon. This reaction replaces the carbonyl carbon with another OH group and also creates an **ether linkage**, which connects the carbons to forms the ring. The ring structures of α-glucose and α-fructose are given in the Section 34 of the *Data booklet*.

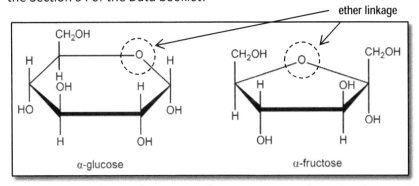

α-glucose   α-fructose

Ring structures drawn this way are knows as **Haworth projections** and show which groups lie above and below the plane of the ring.

Stereoisomerism in monosaccharides (HL)

Carbons 2,3,4 and 5 in the chain structure of glucose are chiral. This means that there are 16 possible stereoisomers of this structure in total, as each chiral centre can have two possible 3-D configurations. In glucose, carbon 3 has the opposite configuration of H and OH compared to carbons 2,4 and 5. There are two mirror image stereoisomers of glucose, labelled D and L. For monosaccharides, these labels refer to the configuration of the chiral carbon atom furthest from the aldehyde or ketone group, which is carbon 5 in the case of glucose and other hexoses.

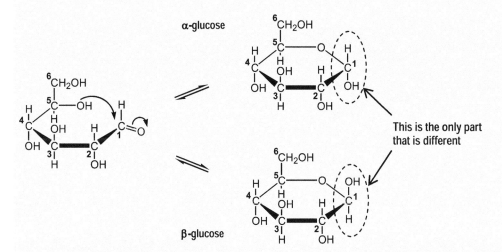

the configuration here decides whether it is D or L

the relative configuration of all the other chiral centres decides whether it is glucose, galactose, or one of the other six possible stereoisomers

L-glucose   D-glucose   L-galactose

The D form of glucose occurs most frequently in nature. Some of the other 14 possible stereoisomers of the glucose structure that are not mirror images of glucose also occur naturally, and include monosaccharides such as galactose and mannose.

During the cyclisation reaction of glucose the chain can turn in two ways so that the OH group formed at carbon 1 will be pointing either 'up' or 'down' as the rings are normally drawn. The two ring forms are given the labels α and β.

α-glucose

This is the only part that is different

β-glucose

Exam Tip

Don't confuse the use of α and β to describe both the ring forms of monosaccharides with the α-helix and β-sheet in the secondary structure of proteins.

Fructose forms α and β ring structures in a similar way to glucose. See the structure of α-fructose from the *Data booklet* shown on the opposite page. β-Fructose has the -OH group on carbon 2 above the plane of the ring, just as β-glucose does for carbon 1.

These groups are swapped from the α-form shown on the opposite page.

β-fructose

Disaccharides

The ring structures of monosaccharides can join together to form disaccharides and polysaccharides. This is by a condensation reaction between two of the OH groups on each molecule to form a **glycosidic linkage**, which is also an ether linkage.

Exam Tip

You will need to practice using the structures of glucose and fructose given in the *Data booklet* to construct the structure of a given disaccharide. For HL, this might involve the α and β forms.

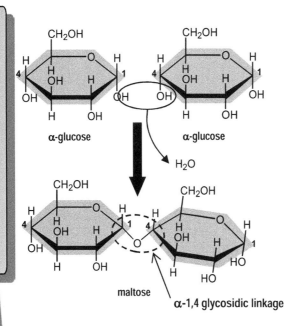

Notice that the α-1,4 glycosidic link causes the next glucose unit to turn slightly. This explains why longer chains of α-glucose, such as those in starch, coil up rather than form straight fibres.

Common disaccharides include **maltose** (shown above), **lactose** (found in milk) and **sucrose** (cane sugar). Sucrose is formed from glucose and fructose connected by a 1,2-glycosidic linkage.

Polysaccharides

Condensation of many monosaccharide molecules into a long chain forms a polysaccharide. Important polysaccharides include starch and cellulose in plants and glycogen in animals.

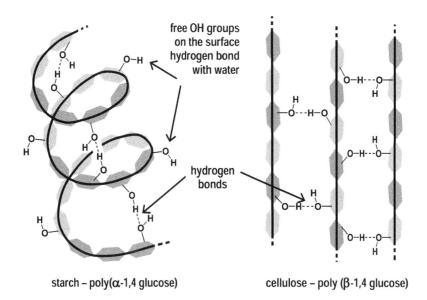

Starch is mainly is a poly(α1-4 glucose) chain that coils to form a globular molecule. This makes it slightly soluble in water due to free –OH groups on the outside of the molecule. This means that it is accessible to enzymes that can break it down to glucose when the organism needs energy. Glucose and other monosaccharides are even more soluble than starch due to the additional −OH groups formed on each molecule by hydrolysis of the glycosidic bond. The solubility of monosaccharides means that they can be rapidly transported in solution to where the energy is needed.

Cellulose is a poly(β1-4 glucose) chain that leads to parallel chains with very few free OH groups on the outside. This is why cellulose can form the insoluble structural material that forms the cell walls of plants.

Dietary fibre (HL)

When starch is eaten by animals, enzymes in the digestive tract hydrolyse it to form glucose. However cellulose remains undigested because mammals do not produce the enzyme *cellulase* needed to catalyse the hydrolysis of β1-4 linkages. Dietary fibre is formed from this undigested cellulose and other plant material. A diet high in fibre is important to help prevent conditions such as diverticulitis, irritable bowel syndrome, constipation, obesity, Crohn's disease, haemorrhoids and diabetes mellitus.

Revision questions

4.1 State two major functions of carbohydrates in the human body. [3]

4.2 State the general formula of a monosaccharide and name two functional groups present in all monosaccharides. [3]

4.3 Describe the structural difference between the straight chain structures of glucose and fructose. [2]

4.4 Draw the structure of sucrose, which is the disaccharide formed from α-glucose and β-fructose linked by an α1-2β glycosidic linkage. [2]   (+ [1] for α/β orientation required for HL only)

4.5 Compare the structural features of starch and cellulose and explain how these relate to their function. [3]   (+ [1] for α/β orientation required for HL only)

4.6 Discuss the importance of cellulose in the human diet and state two conditions that could occur if the diet is deficient in cellulose. (HL only) [3]

5 Vitamins

Vitamins are organic micronutrients that (mostly) cannot be synthesized by the body but must be obtained from suitable food sources.

The structures of three vitamins, retinol (vitamin A), ascorbic acid (vitamin C) and vitamin D are given in section 35 of the *Data booklet*.

Chemistry data booklet, 2015, © IBO

retinol (vitamin A)

ascorbic acid (vitamin C)

vitamin D (D3)

Exam Tip

Questions commonly ask you to identify organic functional groups in given structures, so make sure you know all the groups in the molecules given in the *Data booklet*.

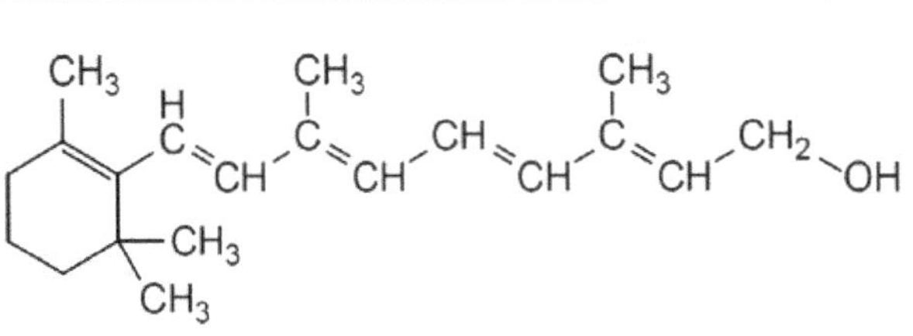

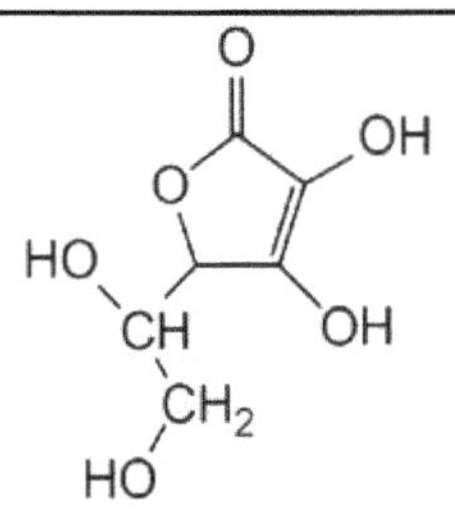

Properties of vitamins

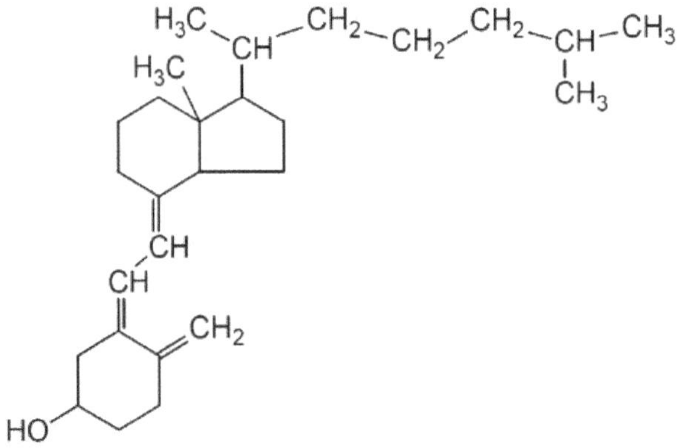

Solubility in water and fat

The solubility of a vitamin in water or in a non-polar solvent (such as a fat) can be predicted by looking at the functional groups in its structure. Vitamins A and D are large molecules containing mainly non-polar hydrocarbon groups that can form significant London forces with non-polar solvents. This is why vitamin A and D are fat-soluble vitamins. Vitamin C is a smaller molecule containing a higher proportion of O-H groups. London forces are not as strong, but the –O-H groups allow it to form strong hydrogen bonds with water. This makes it water-soluble. This means that during cooking, both non-polar and polar vitamins can end up leaving the food as they dissolve in cooking oils and water respectively.

Thermal stability of vitamins

Some vitamins, such as vitamin C, are readily decomposed by heating. This can further reduce the amount of vitamin present in the food after it has been cooked.

Vitamin deficiencies

Dietary deficiencies in vitamins can lead to particular diseases that affect millions of people worldwide. For example a deficiency in:

- vitamin A, leads to xerophthalmia (night blindness)
- vitamin C, leads to scurvy
- vitamin D, leads to rickets (bone malformation)

The causes of nutrient deficiencies in different countries will be related to the availability of different foods to the local population. For example vitamin A deficiency is prevalent in developing countries due to a shortage of the vitamin in the diet, while vitamin D deficiency is increasing in the developed countries, partly as a result of greater protection of the skin from sunlight.

Solutions to vitamin deficiency include:

- providing food rations that are composed of vitamin-rich fresh foods
- providing vitamin supplements
- genetic modification of food crops to contain more vitamins (see Chapter 7).

Revision questions

5.1 Use the structures of vitamin A, vitamin C and vitamin D given in Section 35 of the *Data Booklet* to deduce whether each is water soluble or fat soluble. Explain your choices by reference to their structures and intermolecular forces.   [5]

5.2 Describe and explain two reasons why boiling green vegetables in water leads to a loss of vitamin C from the vegetables.   [3]

5.3 Pellagra is a disease resulting from a deficiency in vitamin B_3. This is common in countries where the people eat mainly rice. Explain why such conditions are more common in the developing world and suggest how these problems may be tackled.   [3]

6 Biochemistry and the environment

(Syllabus section B6)

Xenobiotics

The increased use of synthetic materials and chemicals in industry, agriculture and medicine has led to problems when these substances have entered the environment and affected the ecosystem through their use or disposal. A **xenobiotic** is a chemical that is found in an organism or biological system that is not naturally produced or expected to be present.

The term xenobiotics is often used in the context of pollutants. An example is the increasing problem of antibiotics that are used to treat humans or farm animals becoming present in wastewater. These antibiotics can kill the microorganisms needed to carry out the breakdown of organic matter in sewage treatment plants.

Biomagnification of pollutants

A particular problem with xenobiotics can be **biomagnification**, which is the increase in concentration of a substance in the environment. This can happen in a **food chain**, where each predator in turn eats a relatively large amount of its prey and so accumulates the xenobiotic.

One example is the concentration of the heavy metal mercury in the aquatic environment. This starts with plankton, which absorb the metal ions from the sea. The plankton are eaten by small fish, which are in turn, eaten by large fish. The concentration of mercury in the fish is sufficient to be toxic to humans at the top of the food chain.

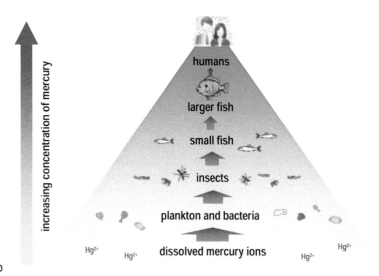

Another example is the accumulation of the pesticide DDT, which has in the past led to a significant decline in the populations of birds of prey at the top of the food chain.

Tackling pollution

Host-guest chemistry

The removal of an unwanted xenobiotic from the environment can be a challenge, as the substance might only be present in relatively small amounts. Also the use of normal chemical methods can cause more problems than are solved, by breaking down or altering other substances that are part of the natural environment.

One solution to this problem is the use of **host–guest chemistry**. This involves the creation of synthetic molecules that mimic some of the actions performed by enzymes in cells.

These larger 'host' molecules bind selectively to the smaller 'guest' molecule or ion, in a similar way to the binding of a substrate to an enzyme at its active site (see charpter 2). The complex formed between the host and guest is called a **supramolecule**. As with enzymes, the guest species is bound to the host molecule by some combination of non-covalent interactions, such as London forces, dipole-dipole forces, hydrogen bonds or ionic bonds. An example of this is the use of zeolite (a giant structure based on aluminium and silicon oxide) to selectively bind non-polar organic hydrocarbon molecules, which either bind to the surface or fit into the interior of the framework using London forces. The diagram shows a zeolite binding a molecule of benzene, which is a carcinogen present in gasoline.

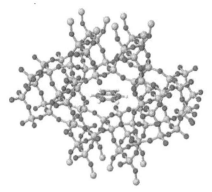

Diagram from: http://www.chemtube3d.com/
solidstate/SS-Z-thetabenzene.htm.

Use of enzymes

Another approach to removing unwanted xenobiotics is the use of enzymes. For example, enzymes have been developed to help in the breakdown of oil spills and other industrial wastes. These enzymes are produced naturally by microorganisms. The microorganisms can be used directly on the waste material, or alternatively the enzyme can be extracted from the organism and concentrated into a formulation that quickly breaks down the unwanted hydrocarbons or other chemicals.

Enzymes, such as proteases or lipases, are also used in **biological detergents** to catalyse the breakdown of protein or fat based stains on clothes. These can improve energy efficiency by enabling effective cleaning at lower temperatures than without using the enzymes.

Biodegradable plastics

Traditional plastics are either polyalkenes, such as poly(ethene), or condensation polymers, such as polyester or nylon. However these do not biodegrade naturally in the environment, leading to problems of disposal. They take up space in landfill sites, as well as being potentially hazardous to wildlife. Many countries now recycle as many plastics as possible. However recycling is often difficult due to difficulties collecting and sorting the different types of plastic. To counter this problem, biodegradable/compostable plastics have been developed that can be consumed or broken down by bacteria or other organisms present in the environment.

One of the most common types of biodegradable plastic is made from starch, the natural polymer made from α-glucose (see chapter 4). This can be easily extracted from corn or vegetables that contain a high level of starch. The flexibility of the plastic can be controlled by adding glycerol, which forms hydrogen bonds with the starch molecules, preventing close contact between the polymer chains. This stops the starch forming regular crystalline solid regions, which makes it less rigid. Uses of starch based polymers include: plastic bags, bin liners and packaging.

Plastics made from starch typically take three to six months to biodegrade, compared to hundreds of years for non-biodegradable plastics. Biodegradable polymers have the added advantage of being renewable, so their manufacture does not use up limited supplies of fossil fuels.

bin liners
made from
corn starch

Green Chemistry

Rather than try to remove unwanted xenobiotics from the environment, a better approach is to try to prevent them getting there in the first place. **Green chemistry**, also called sustainable chemistry, is an approach to chemical research and engineering that seeks to minimize the production and release to the environment of hazardous substances. This involves consideration of a number of criteria, including the following.

- Are processes used that maximise the amount of raw material that ends up in the product? (this can be done by improving both percentage yield and atom economy – see below);
- Does the process avoid the production of waste materials?
- Are renewable materials used as raw materials and energy sources?
- Are non-toxic, environmentally safe substances used throughout?
- Are the processes energy efficient?

There are a number of strategies that can improve the amount of raw material that ends up in the product. Processes that involve fewer steps will usually improve the overall **percentage yield** of the product, as each step will typically involve the loss of some of the material.

Another relatively simple measure that compares the amount of raw material that ends up in the product is calculation of the **atom economy** of the process. An example is the production of the common analgesic, ibuprofen from the raw material, 2-methylpropylbenzene.

2-methylpropylbenzene

original synthesis
6 steps, atom economy 40%

3 steps, atom economy 77%
'greener' synthesis

ibuprofen

The original method involved six steps. However this was replaced by a process involving only three steps, so there is a higher overall percentage yield, as well as a higher atom economy of 77%.

Attempts have been made to assess the 'greenness' of a substance, but can be a challenge for a number of reasons.

1. There might be other hazardous substances or energy costs involved in the overall development and production of a 'green' chemical, for example in the construction of the factory.

2. The use of natural raw materials, such as plant oils, takes up agricultural land that can also be used for food production, leading to problems for the local population.

3. You have to have agreement about how to measure the relative importance of each criterion, which can be difficult, as opinions may vary.

Revision questions

6.1 The insecticide DDT has been shown to increase in concentration from 0.040 mgdm^{-3} in plants to a dangerous level of 13.8 mgdm^{-3} in the tissues of some birds of prey. Calculate the proportional increase in concentration and explain why the concentration is so much higher in birds of prey.   [4]

6.2 Suggest how host-guest chemistry could be used to remove a specific pollutant, such as mercury ions from natural water in the environment.   [2]

6.2 Ethanol can be made by either hydration of ethene with steam, or by fermentation of glucose. Write equations for each process and calculate the atom economy of each process. Although fermentation of glucose has a lower atom economy than hydration of ethene, suggest two reasons why fermentation is still considered to be a greener process than hydration of ethene. [6]

6.4 Describe two challenges in assessing the greenness of a manufactured substance. [2]

7 Nucleic acids (HL only)   (Syllabus section B8)

Nucleotides

A nucleotide is formed by a condensation reaction between a pentose sugar, phosphoric acid and an organic nitrogenous base. Note that at cellular pH, one of the OH groups on the phosphoric acid is ionised to give the dihydrogen phosphate ion, $H_2PO_4^-$

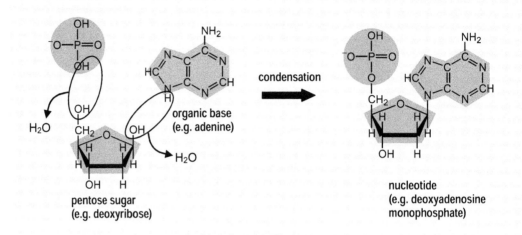

The structures of the two pentose sugars: ribose, deoxyribose and the structures of the five organic bases: adenine (A), guanine (G), cytosine (C), thymine (T) and uracil (U) are given in section 34 of the *Data booklet*.

Chemistry data booklet, 2015, © IBO

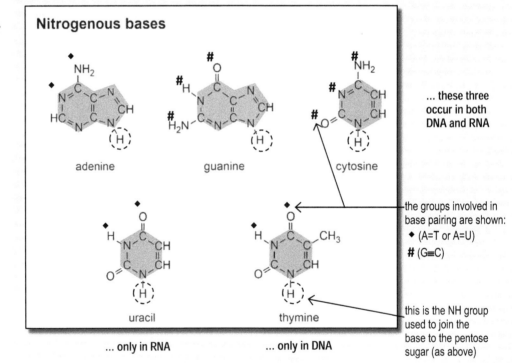

Nucleic acids

Nucleic acids such as DNA and RNA are made from **polynucleotides**, which are condensation polymers made by joining many nucleotides together in a long chain. They are joined by the covalent bonds between the phosphate of one nucleotide and the sugar of the next. This gives a repeating pattern of sugar–phosphate–sugar–phosphate, with a nitrogenous base attached to each sugar along the backbone.

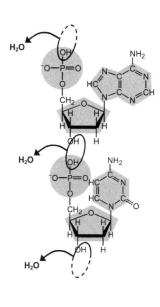

There are three structural differences between DNA and RNA:

- RNA has ribose as its pentose sugar; DNA has deoxyribose, which lacks an oxygen atom on C2,

- RNA has uracil instead of thymine as one of its four organic bases,

- RNA is usually single-stranded; DNA is double-stranded.

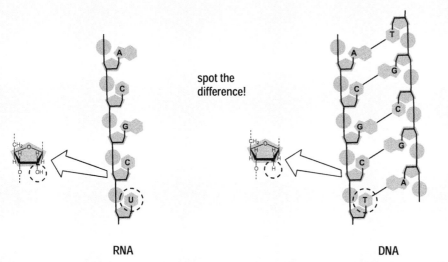

RNA

spot the difference!

DNA

The DNA molecule forms a twisted **double helix** with the two nucleic acid strands spiralling around an axis like a twisted ladder. The double helix molecule is stabilised by both hydrophilic and hydrophobic interactions.

Hydrophilic interactions

The two strands are held together by hydrogen bonding between specific pairs of nucleotide bases. Two hydrogen bonds link adenine (A) to thymine (T) or uracil (U). Three hydrogen bonds link guanine (G) to cytosine (C). This is known as **complementary base pairing**, as each particular base can only pair with one other base.

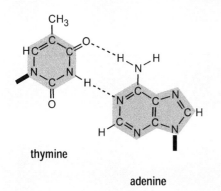

thymine

adenine

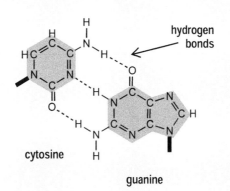

hydrogen bonds

cytosine

guanine

OSC Revision Guide

Hydrophobic interactions

The double helix molecule is also stabilised by London forces acting between the hexagonal and pentagonal rings of the organic bases that are stacked on top of each other up through the centre of the double helix. This is very similar to the forces that act between the hexagonal layers of carbon in graphite.

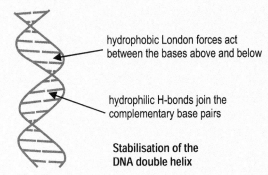

hydrophobic London forces act between the bases above and below

hydrophilic H-bonds join the complementary base pairs

Stabilisation of the DNA double helix

Storage of DNA in the chromosomes of the cell nucleus

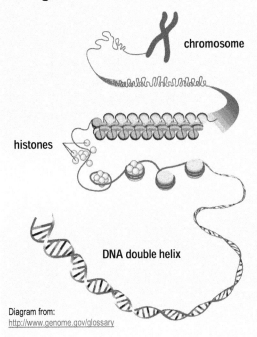

chromosome

histones

DNA double helix

Diagram from:
http://www.genome.gov/glossary

In the nucleus of the cell, the DNA molecules are bound to proteins called **histones**. The combination of DNA and histones make up the **chromosomes** – visible organelles that can be seen under the microscope when the cell is dividing.

The histone proteins have a large number of basic side chains, which are positively charged at cellular pH. The positively charged groups, such as $-NH_3^+$ on the end of the lysine side chain, form ionic bonds with the negatively charged phosphates that alternate along the polynucleotide backbone (see previous page). The phosphates are negatively charged due to loss of H^+ from the free hydroxyl group on the acidic phosphoric acid that joins the deoxyribose sugars together.

DNA replication

The double-stranded structure of DNA allows it to replicate itself exactly before a cell divides. This happens by the two strands coming apart like a zip being undone. Each single strand then acts as a template for the formation of a new complementary strand.

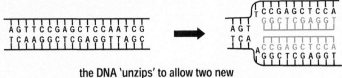

the DNA 'unzips' to allow two new complementary strands of DNA to form

The exact base-pairing ensures that the two new strands are identical to the strands in the original length of DNA.

The genetic code

DNA is the repository of genetic information that an individual inherits from its parents. The information is stored in the sequence of the four bases: G, C, A and T along one strand of the DNA. This sequence of bases is used to determine the primary structure of the proteins that are made by the cell. Each amino acid is coded for by particular sequences of three bases along the strand. This triplet code is known as the **genetic code**, and it is universal for all organisms. For example: the amino acid alanine is coded for by sequences GCU, GCC, GCA or GCG. Note that with four different bases there are 4 x 4 x 4 = 64 different possible sequences of three bases in order. With only 20 naturally occurring 2-amino acids, this means that most of the 2-amino acids are coded by more than one sequence, as in the example above. There are also a few sequences reserved for coding the start and end of the polypeptide chain.

Genetically modified foods

Genetic modification of the DNA of food crops by synthetically altering the sequence of bases, or adding in DNA from other organisms, has been used to increase yields and quality of food crops. One method is to create strains of the plant that are particularly resistant to certain pesticides or herbicides, which can then be used extensively to eradicate pests and weeds without harming the crop. The technique has also been used to produce crops with higher levels of essential nutrients, such as vitamin A, which can help tackle shortages in the diet (see Chapter 5). However despite the advantages, the technique is controversial. Some people oppose its use because:

- local farmers have to become economically dependent on the multinational companies that produce the GM seeds,
- there is a risk of GM plants passing on pesticide resistance etc. to other organisms,
- it encourages increased use of potentially harmful pesticides,
- it reduces the natural variety of species and the variation within the species, that can potentially help the plant develop immunity to diseases in future.

Revision questions

7.1 Use the structure of thymine given on section 34 of the *Data Booklet* to help you draw the structure of the nucleotide deoxythymidine monophosphate. Label each part of the molecule. [5]

7.2 Using the letters 'S', 'P' and 'B' to represent the sugar, phosphate and organic bases respectively, draw a simple diagram to show how these are arranged in short length of RNA. [2]

7.3 State three differences between the structure of DNA and RNA. [3]

7.4 Describe the structure of DNA, and identify the forces involved in stabilising this structure [5]

7.5 Use the structures of guanine and cytosine given on section 34 of the *Data Booklet* to show the bonds involved in base pairing between these two nitrogenous bases. [3]

7.6 Outline how DNA replicates itself. [3]

7.7 Summarise the main benefits and concerns of using genetically modified foods. [4]

8 Biological Pigments (HL only) (Syllabus section B9, plus vision from section B10)

Biological pigments are coloured compounds produced by metabolism. The colour of the pigment is due to the molecule having a highly **conjugated system** – i.e. one with delocalised electrons that spread over many atoms. This happens when there is an alternating single-double bond structure along the chains and/or rings of carbon (or nitrogen) atoms. The p-orbitals overlap, as in benzene, to create one delocalised π-bond along the length of the conjugated system.

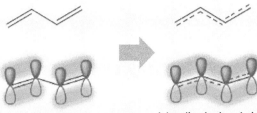

p-orbital overlap to give adjacent π-bonds

delocalised π-bond gives one conjugated system

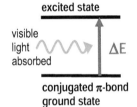

excited state

visible light absorbed

ΔE

conjugated π-bond ground state

If the conjugated system is long enough, it creates a gap in energy levels that corresponds to the energy of some of the wavelengths of light in the visible region of the electromagnetic spectrum. When visible light is shone at the substance it strongly absorbs certain wavelengths, as bonding electrons in the conjugated system are promoted to higher energy levels. The colour of the pigment results from the colours corresponding to the combination of wavelengths <u>not</u> absorbed. The colour wheel in Section 17 of the *Data booklet* gives the colours corresponding to different wavelengths of visible light.

Porphyrin pigments

These include pigments such as *haemoglobin* and *myoglobin* (which are both involved in oxygen transport in animals), *chlorophyll* in plants, and many of the *cytochromes* that play a role in the reduction of oxygen in living cells. Their structures are based on a type of complex ion, known as a **chelate**, where the metal ion is held in place by a large nitrogen-containing ligand that joins to the metal ion by coordinate bonds in several places. This is very similar to the binding of xenobiotics in a host-guest complex – see Chapter 6). In porphyrin pigments, the ligand molecule can be described as **macrocyclic**, as it is composed of a number of linked rings. The structures of chlorophyll and haem are given in section 35 of the *Data booklet*.

Chemistry data booklet, 2015, © IBO

R=CH₃ (chlorophyll a)
R=CHO (chlorophyll b)

chlorophyll

heme B

It can be seen that chlorophyll contains a magnesium ion bound to the porphyrin group, whereas cytochromes, as well as the proteins haemoglobin and myoglobin contain haem group in which an iron(II) ion is bound to the porphyrin group. Note that the conjugated system of alternating single-double bonds that gives rise to the colour spreads right round the macrocyclic ring.

Cytochromes

Cytochromes are proteins that are attached to the inner membrane of mitochondria – the small organelles inside animal and plant cells that carry out aerobic respiration.

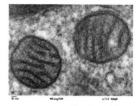

mitochondria

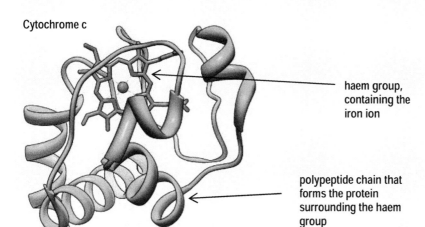

Cytochrome c

haem group, containing the iron ion

polypeptide chain that forms the protein surrounding the haem group

Diagram of the three-dimensional structure of cytochrome c from:
https://en.wikipedia.org/wiki/Cytochrome_c

Cytochromes contain haem groups in which the iron ion interconverts between iron(II) and iron(III) during the redox reactions carried out by the mitochondria. The iron(III) ion is first reduced to iron(II) by accepting an electron (produced from oxidation of carbon compounds).

$$Fe^{3+} + e^- \longrightarrow Fe^{2+}$$

The iron(II) ion then gives up its extra electron to ultimately reduce the oxygen to water.

Oxidation: $4Fe^{2+} \longrightarrow 4Fe^{3+} + 4e^-$

Reduction: $O_2 + 4H^+ + 4e^- \longrightarrow 2H_2O$

This process is known as **electron transport** and takes advantage of the transition element's ability to change readily between two oxidation states. Other cytochromes involved in electron transport use the change in oxidation state between Cu^{2+} to Cu^+ in a similar way.

OSC Revision Guide

haemoglobin
subunits

Oxygen transport by haemoglobin

The haemoglobin molecule is present in the red blood cells that carry oxygen from the lungs to the tissues of the organism. The quaternary structure of haemoglobin molecule consist of four subunits, each with a haem group containing an iron(II) ion. Each subunit can bind one molecule of oxygen.

An iron(II) ion can form a total of six coordinate bonds in an octahedral shape. Four of these are provided by nitrogen atoms in the porphyrin group. A fifth coordinate bond joins the iron(II) ion to a nitrogen on one of the amino acid side-chains of the protein that surrounds the haem group. This leaves a sixth coordinate bond, which can be used to bind an oxygen molecule. However oxygen gas is not a strong Lewis base, so the bond is weak and the binding is easily reversed.

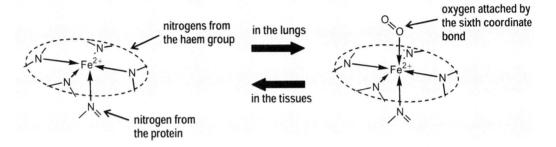

Oxygen dissociation curve for haemoglobin

In the lungs where there is a higher concentration of oxygen, the oxygen molecule can bind to the iron(II) ion. This allows the haemoglobin to transport the oxygen through the blood to the tissues where it is required for respiration. The lower concentration of oxygen in these tissues then shifts the reversible reaction in favour of unbinding the oxygen from the haemoglobin. This can be shown graphically by the oxygen dissociation curve for haemoglobin.

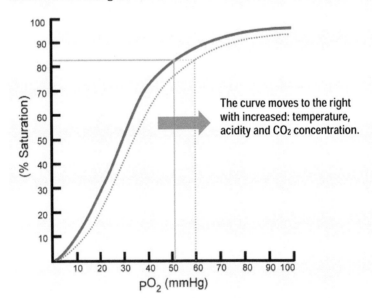

The curve moves to the right with increased: temperature, acidity and CO_2 concentration.

The shape of the line is **sigmoidal**, which describes a line that increases in gradient at lower oxygen concentrations and then levels off at higher concentrations. Note that the concentration of oxygen in the blood is sometimes shown in terms pO_2 in mmHg, which represents the partial pressure of the dissolved oxygen gas.

The line is steepest between 20 and 40 mmHg, which shows that once the haemoglobin has become bound a little oxygen, further binding is then easier, so the % saturation rapidly increases from 25 to 75% over the relatively little increase in the oxygen concentration in the blood. This is very important for its function, as the haemoglobin must be able to bind and then release as much oxygen as possible over the relatively small difference in blood oxygen concentration between the lungs and the tissues.

This behaviour is explained by the fact that once an oxygen molecule has bond to one of the four haemoglobin subunits, a conformational change occurs in the tertiary structure of that subunit. This induces a conformational change in the other three subunits, which makes binding an oxygen molecule by any of these subunits easier. This effect is known as **cooperative binding**.

Factors affecting oxygen saturation

Like all reversible reactions at equilibrium, the % saturation of haemoglobin can be affected by a number of factors. The factors below will shift the oxygen dissociation curve to the right – i.e. the haemoglobin will be less saturated for the given concentration of oxygen.

- An **increase in body temperature**.
- A **decrease in pH** (i.e. the blood becoming more acidic).
- An **increase in carbon dioxide concentration**.

All three of the changes above can happen during exercise. This is because the muscles get hot, produce lactic acid (due to anaerobic respiration), and produce carbon dioxide (due to aerobic respiration). These changes in conditions allow the haemoglobin release more of its oxygen at a time where the muscles particularly need it.

Foetal haemoglobin

A foetus growing inside the mother receives its oxygen across a membrane that separates their two blood systems in the placenta. The oxygen transfers from the haemoglobin in the mother's red blood cells to the haemoglobin in the foetus' red blood cells. In order for the foetal haemoglobin to be able to take sufficient oxygen out of the mother's blood, the foetal haemoglobin has a higher affinity for oxygen. This happens because the foetal haemoglobin has a slightly altered structure compared

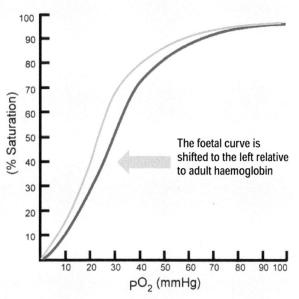

to adult haemoglobin, with two of the four subunits being different. This can be shown by the oxygen saturation curve, which is shifted to the left, to give a higher % saturation at a given temperature.

Carbon monoxide poisoning.

Carbon monoxide is very toxic because it is a much stronger ligand than oxygen. The molecule is of a similar size to oxygen, so fits into the position on the haem group where the oxygen normally binds. Once the carbon monoxide molecule has bound, it cannot be released, due to the greater strength of the coordinate bond. That molecule of haemoglobin is no longer able to carry oxygen. Intake of a large dose of carbon monoxide can put a significant number of the haemoglobin molecules out of action, seriously inhibiting the blood's capacity to carry oxygen.

As the carbon monoxide is binding at the same site as the oxygen, this is similar to competitive inhibition in enzymes (see Chapter 2).

OSC Revision Guide

Chlorophyll and carotenoids

Chlorophyll and carotenoid pigments are found naturally in plants and some bacteria. They are lipid-soluble pigments due to the high proportion of non-polar hydrocarbon areas in their molecules. The structure of chlorophyll as given in section 35 of the *Data booklet* is shown on page 38. Note that it comes in a number of forms, depending on the identity of the R group, with *chlorophyll a* and *chlorophyll b* being the most common.

Carotenoids all have a similar structure to α-carotene and β-carotene, which are given in section 35 of the *Data booklet* and shown below. Note the difference in the position of the carbon-carbon double bond on the right hand ring. In β-carotene, both rings are identical and it is this form that can be split to form retinol (vitamin A) (see Chapter 5 and also page xx later in this chapter).

Chemistry data booklet, 2015, © IBO

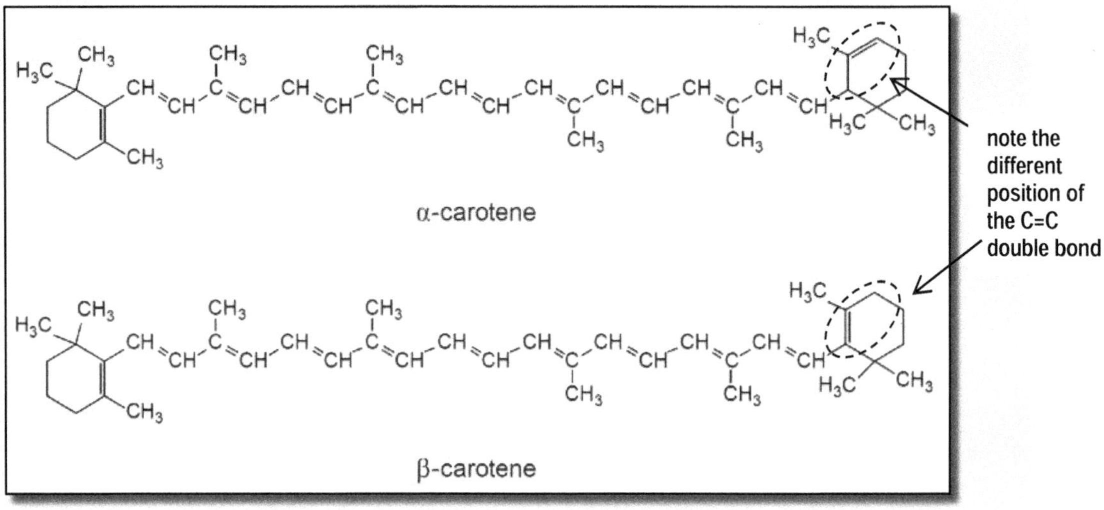

α-carotene

β-carotene

note the different position of the C=C double bond

As with the porphyrin ring in chlorophyll, the carotenoids have a large conjugated π-bond system that allows them to absorb light in the visible region. Carotenoids are responsible for the orange colours in carrots.

Stability of chlorophyll and carotenoids

Chlorophyll is more readily decomposed by **heat** than carotenoids as the metal ion can be lost from the porphyrin ring, particularly at low pH (acidic conditions) when the nitrogen atoms can become protonated.

However both chlorophyll and carotenoids are susceptible to **oxidation**, catalysed by light, due to the large number of carbon-carbon double bonds present. The reaction with oxygen is a free radical mechanism that is very similar to the one responsible for oxidative rancidity in unsaturated fatty acids (see Chapter 3). The ability of carotenoids such as β-carotene to react with oxidising free radicals is beneficial to animals, as this can reduce the concentration of dangerous free radicals in the body. This is why they are described as antioxidants.

Photosynthesis

Photosynthesis is a highly complex series of reactions carried out by plants and some bacteria. Energy from visible light is ultimately used to reduce carbon dioxide and water to form glucose and oxygen gas (see Chapter 1). The pigments involved in absorbing the visible light are: *chlorophyll a*, *chlorophyll b* and a number of carotenoids. The absorption of visible light by the pigments involved in photosynthesis can be shown b y an **absorption spectrum**.

It can be seen that the chlorophylls have two peaks, showing that light that is absorbed in both the blue and red regions of the visible spectrum. This is why chlorophyll looks green to the human eye. Carotenoids only absorb light in the violet and blue region of the spectrum, so look yellow to the human eye (from the combination of red and green colours that are not absorbed). Carotenoids are thought

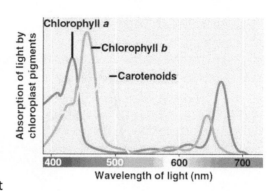

Diagram from:
http://bio1903.nicerweb.com/Locked/media/
lab/photo/key1151.html Peter Chen (2010)

to have a role in harvesting light of wavelengths around 500nm that cannot be absorbed by chlorophyll. The energy from this light can then be passed on to the chlorophyll for photosynthesis. This increases the total amount of energy available to the organism.

Anthocyanins

Anthocyanins are aromatic, water-soluble pigments widely distributed in plants. They typically have colours ranging from red, through purple to blue, and are responsible for the colours of some vegetables like red cabbage and also many flowers. The specific colour of an anthocyanin depends on its structure, but also on the pH and on the presence of metal ions such as Mg^{2+} and Fe^{2+} that form complexes with the pigment molecule. The structures of a typical anthocyanin in both acidic and neutral conditions are given in section 35 of the *Data booklet*.

Chemistry data booklet, 2015, © IBO

increase pH

decrease pH

Note the changes due to protonation here

quinoidal base (blue)

flavylium cation (red)

The **flavylium cation** is present in acidic conditions and is protonated at oxygen on the top left of the molecule as shown. Note that the positive charge is delocalised around the double ring and shown here on the oxygen in the ring. If the pH of solution increases to neutral, the molecule becomes deprotonated, losing the H and the + charge, and forming a ketone group on the top left oxygen to give the **quinoidal base** structure shown. The change from the flavylium cation to the quinoidal base explains the change in colour from red to purple seen when red cabbage is cooked and the pigment escapes from the acidic vacuole in the cells into the neutral water around the cells.

red cabbage

The fact that anthocyanins have two different coloured forms which are conjugate acid-base pairs, makes them useful as **acid-base indicators**, as the colour observed is sensitive to the pH. The colour will change at the pK_a of the acid at which point the observed colour will be a mixture of both forms. (see section 18.3 of the AHL syllabus)

Separation and identification of pigments.

Pigments can be separated and identified using **paper and thin layer chromatography** (see Chapter 2 for a description of paper chromatography). If the pigments are contained within plants, these may need to be crushed to extract he pigment from the plant cells. However unlike with the separation of amino acids there is no need for a locating agent as the pigments are already coloured.

Thin layer chromatography works on similar principles to paper chromatography, except that the stationary phase is a thin layer of fine silicon dioxide powder dried on to a sheet of glass or plastic. The small particle size of the powder can give a more precise result and is better for distinguishing spots with very similar R_f values.

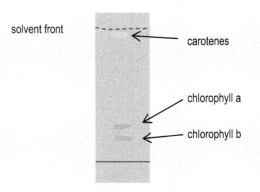

Separation of plant pigments
by thin layer chromatography

With both paper and thin layer chromatography, the polarity of the solvent will be an important factor. A non-polar solvent, such as hexane would be needed to separate chlorophyll or carotenoids, while a polar solvent such as water or ethanol would be better to separate anthocyanins.

Vision chemistry

Vision involves the light activated interconversion of *cis-* and *trans-* isomers of **retinal**. The structures of both stereoisomers are given in section 35 of the *Data booklet*. Note that the two structures given in the *Data booklet*, show that the ring on the left has also been rotated. However as a single carbon-carbon bond can rotate relatively easily, this is a *conformational* isomer rather than a *configurational* isomer. Conformational isomers can interchange with a minimal input of energy, unlike configurational isomers.

The C=C double bonds, such as the one that distinguishes all-*trans-* and 11-*cis-*retinal do not rotate easily, giving the two configurational isomers.

The C-C single bonds rotate easily, giving conformational isomers, such as the rotation shown below

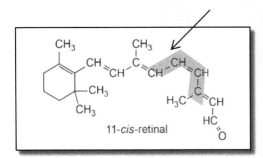

11-*cis-*retinal

isomerisation using energy from a photon of visible light

all-*trans-*retinal

Chemistry data booklet, 2015, © IBO

The 11-*cis*-retinal molecule is bound within a protein called **opsin**, which occurs within the membranes of special structures in the cells of the retina at the back of the eye. **Rhodopsin** is the name for the protein with the retinal bound. The binding site is specific to 11-*cis*-retinal.

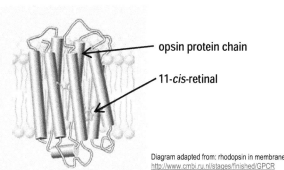

opsin protein chain

11-*cis*-retinal

Diagram adapted from: rhodopsin in membrane
http://www.cmbi.ru.nl/stages/finished/GPCR

When a photon of visible light is absorbed by the 11-*cis*-retinal, the energy temporarily breaks the π-bond, allowing the bond between carbons 11 and 12 to rotate and form all-*trans*-retinal. As the C=C bond cannot rotate easily back, it is now the wrong shape to fit in the binding site and so is released from the opsin protein. The energy is converted to a nerve signal that is sent to the brain. Meanwhile the all-*trans*-retinal is then converted back to 11-*cis*-retinal by enzymes using energy provided by the cell. This can then then bind to another opsin molecule, ready for the process to begin again.

Carotenes and vitamin A as sources of retinal

Carotenes are good natural sources of vitamin A. Two molecules of retinal can be formed by splitting one molecule of β-carotene in the middle of the long unsaturated chain that connects the two identical rings. Note that α-carotene would only form one molecule of retinal, as one of the rings is not the same as that in retinal.

C=C double bond here is broken

Chemistry data booklet, 2015, © IBO

β-carotene

Vitamin A sometimes occurs in the form of retin<u>ol</u>, rather than retinal, and the body can easily interconvert between the two forms. Retinal can be converted to retinol by reduction of the aldehyde group in retinal to the give the primary alcohol group. The structure of retinol is given under the vitamins heading in section 35 of the *Data booklet* (see also Chapter 5).

retinal   + 2[H]   retinol

reduction

oxidation

Revision Questions

8.1 Using the structure of the pigment all-*trans*-retinal given in section 35 of the *Data booklet*, shade the part of the molecule that forms the conjugated π-bond system. [2]

8.2 Explain why the shape of the oxygen dissociation curve for haemoglobin is sigmoidal in shape. [4]

8.3 Explain why carbon monoxide is so toxic to humans. [4]

8.4 Explain the effect of pH on anthocyanins, and state one use of this property. [3]

8.5 Outline the role of vitamin A and opsin in vision. [5]

Answers to Revision Questions

Award one mark for each point ending in a semicolon. Alternative answers are indicated with / .

Proteins – Page 13

2.1

one correct 3-d structure of serine;
both structures correct;   (L and D not required)

2.2 alanine exists is zwitterions;
strong ionic bonding (between ions in alanine);
weaker hydrogen bonding/London forces (between molecules) in lactamide;

2.3

pH 2.5   pH 5.5   pH 9.5

2.4 pKa for benzoic acid = 4.20, so 4.0 = 4.2 + log ([A$^-$]/[HA]);
log([A$^-$]/[HA]) = -0.2   [A$^-$]/[HA] = $10^{-0.2}$;
[A$^-$]/[HA] = 0.631   [HA]/[A$^-$] = **1.58**

2.5

correct amino acids and correct peptide linkages;
correct order;

2.6

2.7 primary structure – covalent bonds in peptide linkages;
secondary structure – hydrogen bonds between peptide N–H and O=C;
tertiary structure – disulfide linkages, hydrogen bonds, ionic bonds and London forces (any three for two marks);
between side chains;

2.8 protein is heated with hydrochloric acid;
amino acid mixture is spotted on paper;
solvent flows up the paper;
amino acids have different solubilities in solvent;
spray with ninhydrin / locating agent;
locations compared with known amino acids / R_f values compared;

2.9 histidine isoelectric point = 7.6, + charge at pH 6.0 , so moves to – electrode;
valine isoelectric point = 6.0, no charge at pH 6.0 , so does not move;
glutamic acid isoelectric point = 3.2, – charge at pH 6.0 ,so moves to + electrode;

2.10 globular: haemoglobin/lysozyme or any named enzyme/insulin etc
fibrous: muscle/keratin/collagen

Enzymes – Page 17

2.11 substrate binds to an active site;
forms an enzyme-substrate complex;
reaction occurs, products leave to reform the enzyme;

2.12 graph axes and labels; (allow enzyme activity for the y axis);
shape of the line;
at low substrate concentration, active sites not filled/enzyme not saturated, so activity is proportional to substrate concentration;
at high substrate concentration, active sites filled/enzyme saturated, so activity is not affected/changed by substrate concentration;

2.13 increase / decrease in temperature; which denatures the enzyme / decreases proportion of molecules with KE ≤ E_a;
change pH; which changes the ionisation of acidic /basic groups involved in maintaining the tertiary structure / active site of the enzyme;
add heavy metal ions; which bind to SH / COOH groups involved in maintaining the tertiary structure / solubility of the enzyme;

2.14 hexokinase;
K_m for hexokinase is (well) below blood glucose concentration
∴ activity is close to V_{max};

2.15
competitive inhibitors	non-competitive inhibitors
bind at the active site	change the shape of the
blocks substrate binding;	enzyme/active site;
higher K_m, same V_{max};	same K_m, lower V_{max};

Lipids – Page 23

3.1 triglycerides;   long term energy storage/insulation/protection/transport of vitamins;
phospholipids; structural component of membranes;
steroids; hormones;

3.2

3.3 saturated fats;
trans-fatty acids;
lead to deposition of cholesterol in the arteries;
causing heart disease/attack / stroke;

3.4 linolenic acid has one extra C=C bond;
they lower LDL levels;
reduced risk of heart disease/attack / stroke;

3.5 grams of I_2 needed to react with 100 g of fat/oil;
moles oil per 100 g = 100/282.5 gmol-1 = 0.3540 mol;
molar mass of I_2 = 2 x 126.90 = 253.8 gmol-1 , so moles of I_2 needed to react with 100 g of fat/oil
= 90 g / 253.8 gmol-1 = **0.3546**;

mol of I_2 needed to react with 1 mol fatty acid = 0.3546 mol / 0.3540 mol-1 = 1.002
∴ **one C=C bond** per molecule;

3.6   condensation reaction;

$$CH_3(CH_2)_{10}COOH + \begin{array}{l} HO-CH_2 \\ HO-CH \\ HO-CH_2 \end{array} \longrightarrow \begin{array}{l} CH_3(CH_2)_{10}COO-CH_2 \\ CH_3(CH_2)_{14}COO-CH \\ C_{17}H_{33}COO-CH_2 \end{array} + 3H_2O$$

with $CH_3(CH_2)_{14}COOH$ and $C_{17}H_{33}COOH$

correct fatty acid formulae (allow molecular formulae);
glycerol;
triglyceride;
3 x water;

3.7   carbohydrates contain a higher proportion of C=O, C-O /O-H bonds/oxygen;
carbohydrates are partially oxidised/release less energy on oxidation;
energy from fat is released more slowly;
fats are less soluble than carbohydrates;

3.8   any value between $-11^\circ C$ and $14^\circ C$;
more C=C bonds than oleic acids, but less than α-linolenic acid;

3.9   advantages: raise melting point; decrease rate of (oxidative) rancidity
disadvantages: formation of trans-fats; increased LDL/risk of heart disease/diabetes/obesity;

3.10   medical use: build up muscle mass to help recovery from injury / starvation;
non-medical use: body-building / enhance athletic performance;
give an unfair advantage to athletes;
can lead to long-term health risks/loss of male characteristics/infertility;

Carbohydrates – Page 27

4.1   immediate energy source;
short term energy reserves;

4.2 $C_n(H_2O)_{2n}$;
carbonyl/ketone;
hydroxyl /alcohol;

4.3   glucose is an aldehyde / has CHO;
fructose is a ketone / has C=O (on the second carbon);

4.4

sucrose

correct structures of glucose and fructose (ignoring α/β orientation)
glycosidic link between C1 of glucose and C2 of fructose;
correct α/β orientation of glucose, fructose and the 1-2 glycosidic link (HL only);

4.5
starch	cellulose
α-1,4 glycosidic linkages	β-1,4 glycosidic linkages (HL only);
globular/	fibrous/
OH groups on outside	OH groups between chains;
soluble	insoluble;
used as energy store	used as a structural material/for plant cell wall;

4.6   dietary fibre;
(any two from) diverticulitis, irritable bowel syndrome, constipation, obesity, Crohn's disease, haemorrhoids, diabetes mellitus;;

Vitamins – Page 29

5.1   vitamin A and D are fat soluble, vitamin C is water soluble;
vitamin A and D have a large (non-polar) hydrocarbon part;
vitamin C has many O-H groups;
vitamin A and D have London forces; vitamin C can H-bond;

5.2   vitamin C is water soluble;
vitamin C dissolves into cooking water during boiling;
vitamin C is decomposed by heat;

5.3   limited amount/variety of food available to poor people in the developed world;
solutions: food rations / nutritional supplements / genetic modification of crops; (any two);

Biochemistry and the environment – page 33

6.1   proportional increase = 13.8/0.040 = **345** ;
increase is due to biomagnification;
plants are at bottom of the food chain, birds of prey are at the top;
DDT becomes more concentrated higher up the food chain as the mass of the predator is much less than the food it eats;

6.2   the 'host' is a supramolecule/large molecule which binds specifically to the 'guest' Hg^{2+} ions;
the natural water is passed through a filter where the host molecule is immobilised;

6.3 $C_2H_4 + H_2O \rightarrow C_2H_5OH$;
$C_6H_{12}O_6 \rightarrow 2C_2H_5OH + 2CO_2$;
atom economy by hydration = **100%** (as no other products)
atom economy by fermentation =
$(2 \times 46.08)/180.18 = $ **51.1%** ;

(any two of) glucose is a renewable raw material / fermentation requires less energy / production of ethene (from crude oil) is potentially more polluting (due to chance of oil spills etc) / hydration needs a (phosphoric/sulfuric) acid catalyst;;

6.4   (any two of the following)
difficult to quantify hazardous substances/energy involved in the development/construction of industrial plants,
land used for growing crops to make renewable substances prevents food production for local populations,
opinions vary about the relative importance of different 'greenness' criteria;;

Nucleic Acids – Page 37

7.1

phosphate;

thymine; correct connection to the sugar;

deoxyribose; correct structure of sugar and phosphate; (allow any ionisation)

7.2   S – P – S – P – S – P – S – P
       | | | |
       B   B   B   B

alternating S-P;
one B on each S;

7.3 | **DNA** | **RNA**
deoxyribose sugar | ribose sugar;
contains thymine | contains uracil;
double stranded | single stranded;

7.4 double helix;
each strand, alternating sugar-phosphate;
nitrogenous base attached to each sugar;
hydrogen bonds between specific base pairs;
London forces between bases above and below;

7.5 one mark for each H-bond;;;

7.6 DNA 'unzips';
new lengths of complementary DNA form on both exposed strands;
new double strands separate to give two identical molecules;

7.7 **benefits** (any two from)
increased/consistent yield/quality / increased vitamin/nutrient content / increased resistance to pests;;

concerns (any two from)
dependence of local farmers on multinational corporations / reduces natural variation / resistance passed on to weeds / encourages use of pesticides

Biological pigments – Page 45

8.1

main carbon chain shaded; including the ring C=C and C=O;

8.2 due to cooperative binding;
conformational change occurs in one subunit on binding O_2;
which induces a conformational change in the remaining three subunits;
leading to greater affinity of the other three subunits for O_2;

8.3 (any four from) CO acts as a ligand/Lewis base;
CO binds to Fe^{2+} ions in haemoglobin;
binding is irreversible/very strong;
CO acts as a competitive inhibitor/prevents O_2 binding;
reduces the blood's ability to carry O_2;

8.4 causes a change in colour;
due to (de)protonation;
can be used as acid/base indicators;

8.5 vitamin A is retinal/retinol;
cis-retinal is bound to opsin (to give rhodopsin);
light causes isomerisation from cis to trans;
the resulting conformational change in opsin sends a signal to the brain;
trans converted back to cis;

Acknowledgements:

Screenshots from sections 1, 33, 34 and 35 of the IB Chemistry data booklet, Third Edition (Updated May 2015), © International Baccalaureate Organisation. Used with permission.

Pictures and diagrams

Olive Oil picture – page 21
https://commons.wikimedia.org/wiki/File:Oli_de_l%27Empord%C3%A0.jpg
Butter picture – page 22
https://commons.wikimedia.org/wiki/File:Western-pack-butter.jpg
Testosterone supplement bottle picture – page 23
https://commons.wikimedia.org/wiki/File:Depo-testosterone_200_mg_ml_crop.jpg
Vegetables cooking picture – page 28
http://www.amazon.co.uk/Multi-Use-Pan-Saucepan-Vegetable/dp/B00TZSMOIE
Benzene in zeolite structure – page 31
http://www.chemtube3d.com/solidstate/SS-Z-thetabenzene.htm
Histone picture – page 36
National Institutes of Health. National Human Genome Research Institute. "Talking Glossary of Genetic Terms." http://www.genome.gov/glossary/
Starch bag picture
http://www.wheeliebindirect.co.uk/Biodegradable/Compostable-Kitchen-Corn-Starch-Bio-Bin-Bags
Mitochondria electron micrograph – page 39
https://commons.wikimedia.org/wiki/File:Mitochondria,_mammalian_lung_-_TEM.jpg
Cytochrome c structure – page 39
https://en.wikipedia.org/wiki/Cytochrome_c#/media/File:Cytochrome_C.png
Haemoglobin subunits – page 40
http://pubs.rsc.org/services/images/RSCpubs.ePlatform.Service.FreeContent.ImageService.svc/ImageService/ChapterImage/bk9781782620228/BK9781782620228-00001/bk9781782620228-00001-f5_hi-res.gif
Chlorophyll spectrum – Peter Chen (2010) – page 43
http://bio1903.nicerweb.com/Locked/media/lab/photo/key1151.html
Red cabbage picture – page 43
https://literarysara.files.wordpress.com/2015/02/cabbage.jpg
Rhodopsin in membrane structure – page 45
http://www.cmbi.ru.nl/stages/finished/GPCR/

IBDP REVISION COURSES

Summary

Who are they for?
Students about to take their final IBDP exams (May or November)

Locations include:
Oxford, UK
Rome, Italy
Brussels, Belgium
Dubai, UAE
Adelaide, Sydney & Melbourne, AUS
Munich, Germany

Duration
1.5 days per subject
Students can take multiple subjects

The most successful IB revision courses worldwide

Highly-experienced IB teachers and examiners

Every class is tailored to the needs of that particular group of students

Features

- Classes grouped by grade (UK)
- Exam skills and techniques – typical traps identified
- Exam practice
- Pre-course online questionnaire to identify problem areas
- Small groups of 8–10 students
- 24-hour pastoral care.

Revising for the final IB exams without expert guidance is tough. Students attending OSC Revision Courses get more work done in a shorter time than they could possibly have imagined.

With a different teacher, who is confident in their subject and uses their experience and expertise to explain new approaches and exam techniques, students rapidly improve their understanding. OSC's teaching team consists of examiners and teachers with years of experience – they have the knowledge and skills students need to get top grades.

The size of our Oxford course gives some particular advantages to students. With over 1,000 students and 300 classes, we can group students by grade – enabling them to go at a pace that suits them.

Students work hard, make friends and leave OSC feeling invigorated and confident about their final exams.

We understand the needs of IBDP students – our decades of experience, hand-picked teachers and intense atmosphere can improve your grades.

> "I got 40 points overall, two points up from my prediction of 38, and up 7 points from what I had been scoring in my mocks over the years, before coming to OSC. Thank you so much for all your help!"
>
> OSC Student

Please note that locations and course features are subject to change - please check our website for up-to-date details.

Find out more: 🏠 **osc-ib.com/revision** 📱 **+44 (0)1865 512802**

MID IBDP SUMMER PROGRAMMES

Summary

Who is it for?
For students entering their final year of the IB Diploma Programme

Locations include:
Harvard and MIT, USA
Cambridge, UK

Duration
Min. 1 week, max. 6 weeks
1 or 2 IB subjects per week

- Improve confidence and grades
- Highly-experienced IB teachers and examiners
- Tailored classes to meet students' needs
- Wide range of available subjects
- Safe accommodation and 24-hour pastoral care

Features

- Morning teaching in chosen IB subject
- 2nd IB subject afternoon classes
- IB Skills afternoon classes
- One-to-one Extended Essay Advice, Private Tuition and University Guidance options
- Small classes
- Daily homework
- Unique IB university fair
- Class reports for parents
- Full social programme.

By the end of their first year, students understand the stimulating and challenging nature of the IB Diploma.

They also know that the second year is crucial in securing the required grades to get into their dream college or university.

This course helps students to avoid a 'summer dip' by using their time effectively. With highly-experienced IB teachers, we consolidate a student's year one learning, close knowledge gaps, and introduce some year two material.

In a relaxed environment, students develop academically through practice revision and review. They are taught new skills, techniques, and perspectives – giving a real boost to their grades. This gives students an enormous amount of confidence and drive for their second year.

The whole experience was incredible. The university setting was inspiring, the friends I made, and the teaching was first-class. I feel so much more confident in myself and in my subject.

OSC Student

Please note that locations and course features are subject to change - please check our website for up-to-date details.

Find out more: osc-ib.com/mid +44 (0)1865 512802